Workbook

Progress in
Mathematics

SADLIER-OXFORD

Catherine D. LeTourneau

with

Elinor R. Ford

Sadlier-Oxford
A Division of William H. Sadlier, Inc.
www.sadlier-oxford.com

Contributing Illustrators: Bernard Adnet, Sarah Beise, Mary Bono, Mircea Catusnu, Georgia Cawley, Lee Duggan, Dave Garbot, Bob Holt, Nathan Jarvis, Gary Johnson, Dave Jonason, Dean Macadam, P.T. Pie, Dirk Wunderlich

---

Requests for permission to make copies of any part of the work should be mailed to:
Permissions Department
William H. Sadlier, Inc.
9 Pine Street
New York, New York 10005-4700

S is a registered trademark of William H. Sadlier, Inc.

Printed in the United States of America

ISBN 978-0-8215-5101-1

5 6 7 8 9   HESS   19 18 17 16

Contents

ℂ Denotes Common Core lesson.

iv

ℂ Denotes Common Core lesson.

Measurement

Add 2-Digit Numbers

Subtract 2-Digit Numbers

Fractions and Probability

C Denotes Common Core lesson.

Additional Common Core Contents

Numbers 1 Through 4

Name _____

Numbers show how many.

1 one

2 two

3 three

4 four

How many bugs?
Write the number word and the number.

1.

two 2

2.

one 1

3.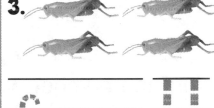

four 4

4.

three 3

5.

6.

7.

8.

9.

Use with Lesson 1-1, pages 3–4 in the Student Book.
Then go to Lesson 1-2, pages 5–6 in this Student Book.

one 1

Numbers 5 and 0

Name _____

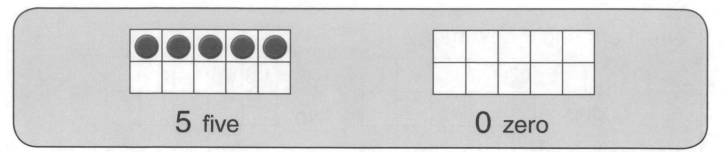

5 five   0 zero

Write how many bugs.

1.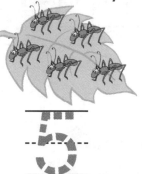

5

2.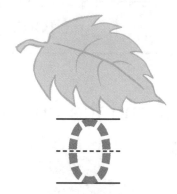

0

3.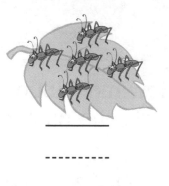

_____
- - - - - - - -
_____

Write the number word and the number.

4.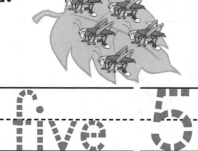

five 5

5.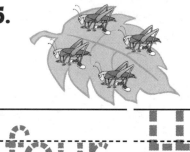

four 4

6.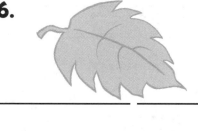

_____ _____

Write the number word.
Draw dots for each number.

7. _____
5 - - - - - - -
_____

8. _____
0 - - - - - - -
_____

9. _____
4 - - - - - - -
_____

Use with Lesson 1-2, pages 5–6 in the Student Book.
Then go to Lesson 1-3, pages 7–8 in the Student Book.

Numbers 6 Through 9

Name _____

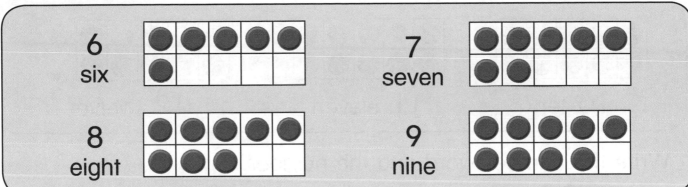

Write the number word and the number.

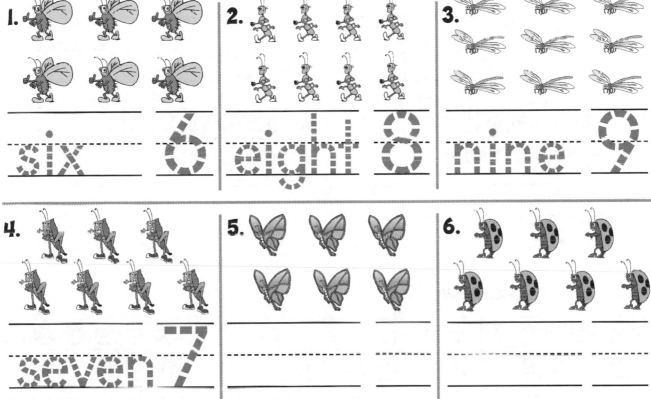

1. six 6

2. eight 8

3. nine 9

4. seven 7

5.

6.

7.

8.

9.

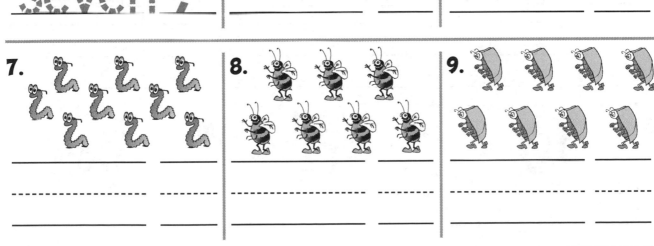

Use with Lesson 1-3, pages 7–8 in the Student Book.
Then go to Lesson 1-4, page 9–10 in the Student Book.

three **3**

Numbers 10 Through 12

Name _____

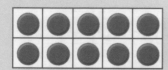	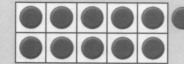	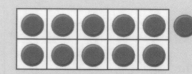
10 ten	11 eleven	12 twelve

Write the number word and the number.

1.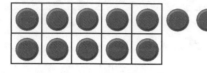

2.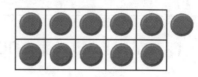

3.

4.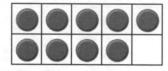

Write the number word.

5.

_____

- - - - - - - - - -

_____

6.

_____

- - - - - - - - - -

_____

7.

_____

- - - - - - - - - -

_____

8.

_____

- - - - - - - - - -

_____

9.

_____

- - - - - - - - - -

_____

10.

_____

- - - - - - - - - -

_____

Use with Lesson 1-4, pages 9–10 in the Student Book.
Then go to Lessons 1-5 and 1-6, pages 11–16 in the Student Book.

One Fewer, One More

Name _____

3 ☐ is one fewer than 4 ■.   5 ☐ is one more than 4 ■.

Draw one more. Write the number.

1.

2.

_____
- - - - - -
_____

3.

_____
- - - - - -
_____

4.

_____
- - - - - -
_____

✗ to show one fewer. Write the number.

5.

6.

_____
- - - - - -
_____

7.

_____
- - - - - -
_____

8.

_____
- - - - - -
_____

Use with Lesson 1-6, pages 15–16 in the Student Book.
Then go to Lesson 1-7, pages 17–18 in the Student Book.

five **5**

Order
0 Through 12

Name _____

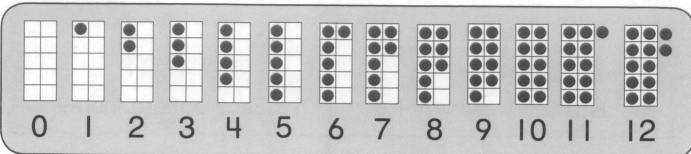

0 1 2 3 4 5 6 7 8 9 10 11 12

Write how many. Then order the numbers.

1. 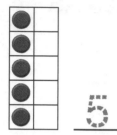 5  ___   ___   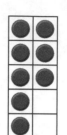 ___

_____, _____, _____, _____

2. 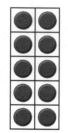 ___   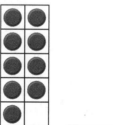 ___   ___   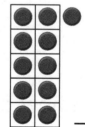 ___

_____, _____, _____, _____

Write the missing numbers.

3. 4, 5, 6, ___   **4.** ___, 9, 10, ___

5. ___, 3, ___, 5   **6.** ___, ___, 2, 3

7. ___, 10, 11, ___   **8.** 6, ___, ___, 9

Use with Lesson 1-7, pages 17–18 in the Student Book.
Then go to Lesson 1-8, pages 19–20 in the Student Book.

Count On

Name _____

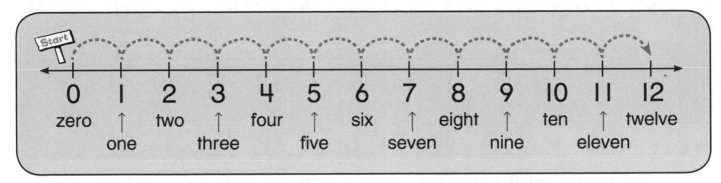

0 1 2 3 4 5 6 7 8 9 10 11 12

zero ↑ two ↑ four ↑ six ↑ eight ↑ ten ↑ twelve
  one   three   five   seven   nine   eleven

Count on. Write the missing numbers.

1.

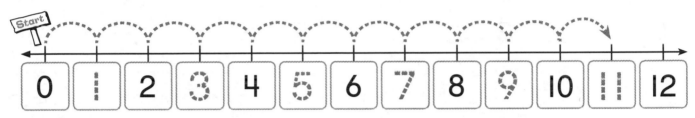

0 1 2 3 4 5 6 7 8 9 10 11 12

2.

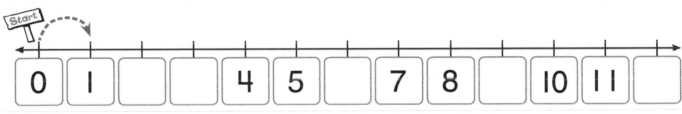

0 1 __ __ 4 5 __ 7 8 __ 10 11 __

3.

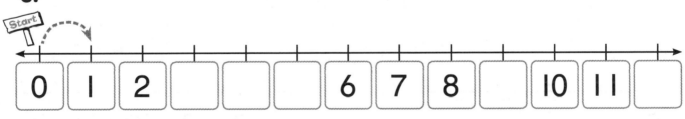

0 1 2 __ __ __ 6 7 8 __ 10 11 __

4.

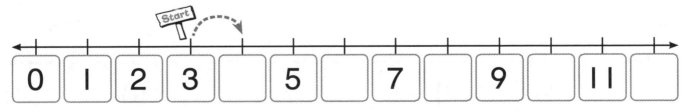

0 1 2 3 __ 5 __ 7 __ 9 __ 11 __

Ⓒ Use with Lesson 1-8, pages 19–20 in the Student Book.
   Then go to Lesson 1-9, pages 21–22 in the Student Book.

Count Back

Name _____

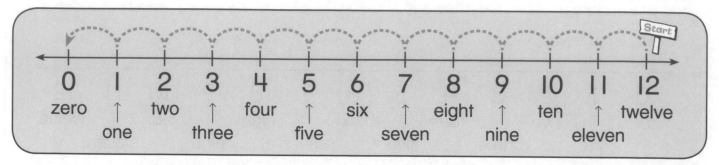

0	1	2	3	4	5	6	7	8	9	10	11	12
zero	↑	two	↑	four	↑	six	↑	eight	↑	ten	↑	twelve
	one		three		five		seven		nine		eleven	

Count back. Write the missing numbers.

1.

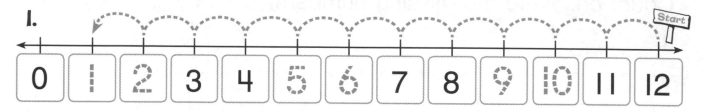

0	1	2	3	4	5	6	7	8	9	10	11	12

2.

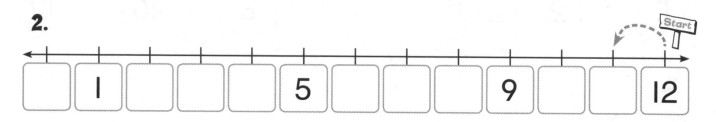

	1			5			9			12

3.

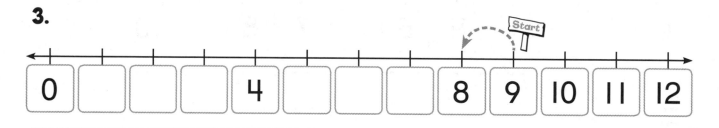

0				4				8	9	10	11	12

4.

0						6	7	8	9	10	11	12

5.

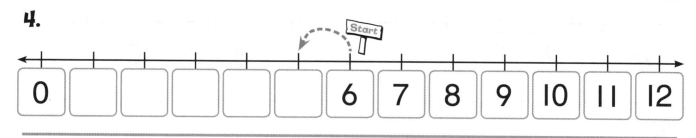

		2		4	5		7		9	10		12

8 eight

Before, Between, After

Name _____

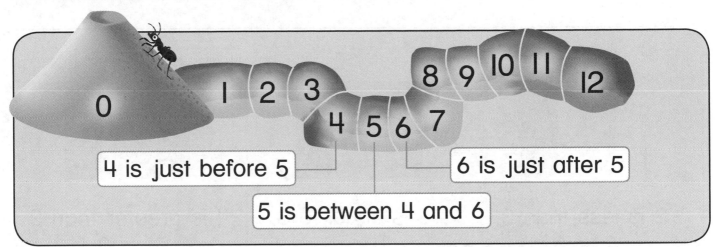

4 is just before 5

6 is just after 5

5 is between 4 and 6

1. Write the number that comes just before.

___4___ , 5   ___ , 4   ___ , 3   ___ , 8

___ , 2   ___ , 9   ___ , 12   ___ , 10

___ , 6   ___ , 11   ___ , 1   ___ , 7

2. Write the number that comes just after.

8, ___9___   1, ___   9, ___   3, ___

5, ___   7, ___   10, ___   0, ___

11, ___   4, ___   2, ___   6, ___

3. Write the number that comes between.

8, ___9___, 10   7, ___, 9   1, ___, 3   5, ___, 7

0, ___, 2   6, ___, 8   2, ___, 4   3, ___, 5

Use with Lesson 1-10, pages 23–24 in the Student Book.
Then go to Lesson 1-11, pages 25–26 in the Student Book.

nine **9**

Compare

Name _____

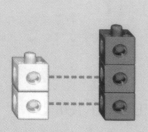 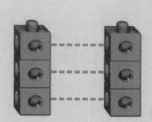 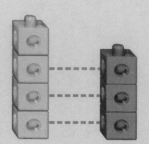

2 is less than 3	3 is equal to 3	4 is greater than 3
2 < 3	3 = 3	4 > 3

Write <, =, or >.

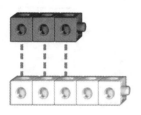 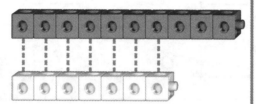 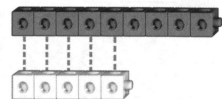

1. 3 ◁ 5

2. 10 ◯ 7

3. 9 ◯ 5

4. 8 ◯ 12

5. 6 ◯ 10

6. 8 ◯ 8

7. 9 ◯ 9

8. 11 ◯ 9

9. 6 ◯ 3

10. twelve ◯ ten

11. seven ◯ eight

12. nine ◯ eleven

13. eight ◯ six

Use with Lesson 1-11, pages 25–26 in the Student Book.
Then go to Lesson 1-12, pages 29–30 in the Student Book.

Ordinals 1st Through 10th

Name _____

| first | second | third | fourth | fifth | sixth | seventh | eighth | ninth | tenth |
| 1st | 2nd | 3rd | 4th | 5th | 6th | 7th | 8th | 9th | 10th |

1. Circle the position of each bug.

	(2nd)	7th	3rd
	2nd	5th	3rd
	4th	1st	10th
	9th	8th	4th
	2nd	10th	6th

2. Color the box. Start at the left.

tenth

eighth

seventh

ninth

sixth

Use with Lesson 1-12, pages 29–30 in the Student Book.
Then go to Lesson 1-13, pages 31–32 in the Student Book.

Ordinals: From Top or Bottom

Name _____

Look at the bugs on the tree.
Write the ordinal number for each bug.

1.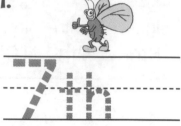

7th _____

2.

_____

3.

_____

4.

_____

5.

_____

6.

_____

7.

_____

8.

_____

9.

_____

10.

_____

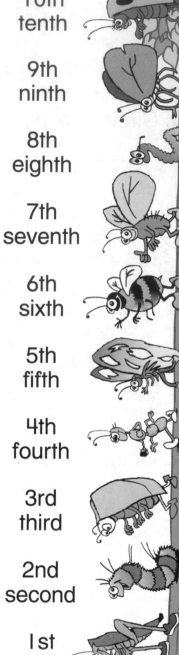

10th
tenth

9th
ninth

8th
eighth

7th
seventh

6th
sixth

5th
fifth

4th
fourth

3rd
third

2nd
second

1st
first

Use with Lesson 1-13, pages 31–32 in the Student Book.
C Then go to Lesson 1-14, pages 33–34 in the Student Book.

Problem-Solving Strategy: Act It Out

Read ▶ Lee sees 5 .
Roland sees 2 more than Lee.
How many does Roland see?

Plan ▶ Use ⬜ and ⬛ to act out the problem.

Write ▶

Lee	Roland
▢▢▢▢▢	▢▢▢▢▢▣▣

Count Roland's cubes.

Roland sees __7__ .

Check ▶ Draw a picture to check.

Act it out.

1. Paula finds 7 🦋.
Ricky finds one fewer 🦋 than Paula.
How many 🦋 does Ricky find?   Ricky finds _____ 🦋.

---

2. Iris catches 3 🐛.
Fred catches 3 more 🐛 than Iris.
How many 🐛 does Fred catch?   Fred catches _____ 🐛.

---

3. Bobby is fifth in line.
Mari is tenth in line.
How many children are between them?   _____ children

---

4. Juan draws 12 🐞.
Mary draws 2 fewer 🐞 than Juan.
How many 🐞 does Mary draw?   Mary draws _____ 🐞.

C Use with Lesson 1-14, pages 33–34 in the Student Book.
C Then go to Lesson 1-15, pages 35–36 in the Student Book.

thirteen **13**

Problem-Solving Applications: Mixed Strategies

Name _____

Read ▶ Plan ▶ Write ▶ Check

Strategy File

Act It Out
Draw a Picture

Use a strategy you have learned.

1. Raul has a number between 5 and 10.
It is one fewer than 9.
What number does Raul have?

6, 7, 8, 9

Raul has number __8__.

---

2. Jodi has 11 .
Rob has 1 more than Jodi.
How many does Rob have?

Rob has ____ .

---

3. Saul is third in line.
Enid is last in line.
There are 3 children between them.
What position is Enid in line?

_____

- - - - - - - - - - - -

Enid is _____ in line.

---

4. Jed caught 3 .
Sally caught 1 more than Jed.
How many did Sally catch?

Sally caught ____ .

C Use with Lesson 1-15, pages 35–36 in the Student Book.

Understanding Addition

Name _____

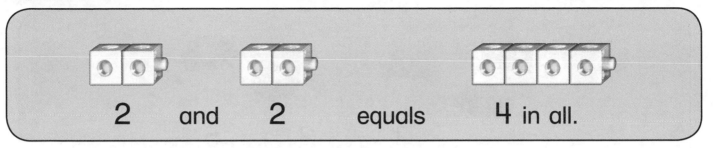

2 and 2 equals 4 in all.

Join 🔲 to model each addition story.
Write the numbers.

1.

____3____ 🐟 and ____2____ 🐟 equals ____5____ in all.

2.

____ 🦎 and ____ 🦎 equals ____ in all.

3.

____ 🐰 and ____ 🐰 equals ____ in all.

4.

____ 🦆 and ____ 🦆 equals ____ in all.

C Use with Lesson 2-1, pages 51–52 in the Student Book.
C Then go to Lesson 2-2, pages 53–54 in the Student Book.

fifteen **15**

Addition Sentences

$$3 + 2 = 5$$
plus   equals

$3 + 2 = 5$ is an addition sentence.

Add. Write each addition sentence.

1.

$$\underline{4} + \underline{2} = \underline{6}$$

2.

$$\underline{} + \underline{} = \underline{}$$

3.

$$\underline{} + \underline{} = \underline{}$$

4.

$$\underline{} + \underline{} = \underline{}$$

5.

$$\underline{} + \underline{} = \underline{}$$

6.

$$\underline{} + \underline{} = \underline{}$$

7.

$$\underline{} + \underline{} = \underline{}$$

8.

$$\underline{} + \underline{} = \underline{}$$

Use with Lesson 2-2, pages 53–54 in the Student Book.
Then go to Lesson 2-2A, pages 175–176 in this Workbook.

Sums Through 6

Name _____

You can write an addition fact in two ways.

$$\begin{array}{r} 3 \\ +1 \\ \hline 4 \end{array}$$ addend
addend
sum

$$3 + 1 = 4$$
addend   addend   sum

Add.

1.

_3_ + _2_ = _5_

2.

$0 + 4 = $ ____

3.

$1 + 2 = $ ____

4.

$1 + 1 = $ ____

5.

$$\begin{array}{r} 0 \\ +2 \\ \hline 2 \end{array}$$

6.

$$\begin{array}{r} \\ + \\ \hline \end{array}$$

7.

$$\begin{array}{r} \\ + \\ \hline \end{array}$$

8.

$3 + 3 = $ ____

9.

$2 + 4 = $ ____

Use with Lesson 2-3, pages 55–56 in the Student Book.
Then go to Lesson 2-4, pages 57–58 in the Student Book.

seventeen **17**

Related Addition Facts

Name _____

Change the order of the addends and get the same sum.

| Horizontal | Vertical |

Horizontal
$$3 + 1 = 4$$
$$1 + 3 = 4$$

Vertical

$$\begin{array}{r} 3 \\ +1 \\ \hline 4 \end{array} \qquad \begin{array}{r} 1 \\ +3 \\ \hline 4 \end{array}$$

Add. Write the related addition fact.

1.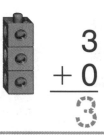
$$\begin{array}{r} 3 \\ +0 \\ \hline 3 \end{array} \qquad \begin{array}{r} 3 \\ + \\ \hline 3 \end{array}$$

2.
$$\begin{array}{r} 5 \\ +1 \\ \hline \end{array} \qquad \begin{array}{r} \\ + \\ \hline \end{array}$$

3.
$$\begin{array}{r} 1 \\ +2 \\ \hline \end{array} \qquad \begin{array}{r} \\ + \\ \hline \end{array}$$

4.
$$\begin{array}{r} 0 \\ +6 \\ \hline \end{array} \qquad \begin{array}{r} \\ + \\ \hline \end{array}$$
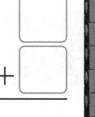

5.
$$\begin{array}{r} 0 \\ +4 \\ \hline \end{array} \qquad \begin{array}{r} \\ + \\ \hline \end{array}$$

6.
$$\begin{array}{r} 2 \\ +3 \\ \hline \end{array} \qquad \begin{array}{r} \\ + \\ \hline \end{array}$$
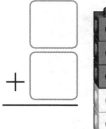

7.

$$1 + 4 = \underline{\quad}$$

$$\underline{\quad} + \underline{\quad} = \underline{\quad}$$

8.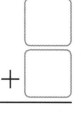

$$3 + 2 = \underline{\quad}$$

$$\underline{\quad} + \underline{\quad} = \underline{\quad}$$

18 eighteen

Sums of 11 and 12

Name _____

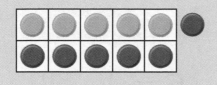
$$5$$
$$+\ 6$$
$$\overline{11}$$

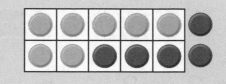
$$7$$
$$+\ 5$$
$$\overline{12}$$

Find the sum.

1.

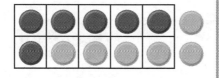

$6 + 6 = \underline{12}$ | $8 + 3 = \underline{}$ | $4 + 8 = \underline{}$

2.

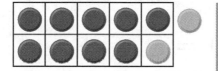  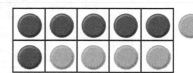

$9 + 2 = \underline{}$ | $5 + 7 = \underline{}$ | $6 + 5 = \underline{}$

Find the sum. Use a ▦ and ⬤ to check.

3.
$$4 \quad\quad 4 \quad\quad 3 \quad\quad 9 \quad\quad 5 \quad\quad 2$$
$$+\ 8 \quad +\ 7 \quad +\ 9 \quad +\ 2 \quad +\ 7 \quad +\ 9$$
$$\overline{12}$$

4. $8 + 4 = \underline{}$ | $6 + 5 = \underline{}$ | $7 + 4 = \underline{}$

5. $3 + 8 = \underline{}$ | $7 + 5 = \underline{}$ | $6 + 6 = \underline{}$

6. $9 + 3 = \underline{}$ | $5 + 6 = \underline{}$ | $9 + 2 = \underline{}$

7. $4 + 7 = \underline{}$ | $5 + 7 = \underline{}$ | $3 + 9 = \underline{}$

C Use with Lesson 2-7, pages 63–64 in the Student Book.
Then go to Lesson 2-8, pages 67–68 in the Student Book.

Other Names for Numbers

Name _____

$5 = 3 + 2$ $5 = 2 + 3$ $5 = 1 + 4$

Write two ways to show each number.

1.

$5 = \underline{4} + \underline{1}$

$5 = \underline{} + \underline{}$

2.

$10 = \underline{} + \underline{}$

$10 = \underline{} + \underline{}$

3.

$8 = \underline{} + \underline{}$

$8 = \underline{} + \underline{}$

4.

$3 = \underline{} + \underline{}$

$3 = \underline{} + \underline{}$

5.

$9 = \underline{} + \underline{}$

$9 = \underline{} + \underline{}$

6.

$12 = \underline{} + \underline{}$

$12 = \underline{} + \underline{}$

Use with Lesson 2-8, pages 67–68 in the Student Book.
Then go to Lessons 2-9 and 2-10, pages 69–71 in the Student Book.

Number-Line Addition

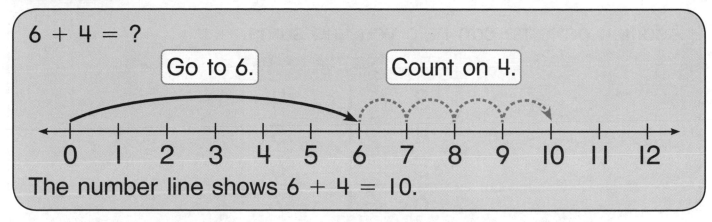

$6 + 4 = ?$

Go to 6.   Count on 4.

The number line shows $6 + 4 = 10$.

Write the addition sentence shown for each number line.

I.

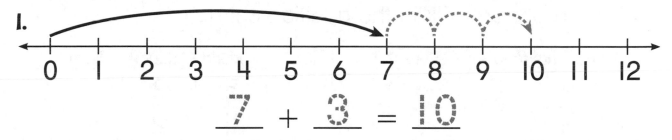

$\underline{7} + \underline{3} = \underline{10}$

2.

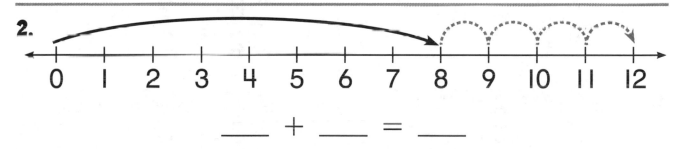

___ + ___ = ___

3.

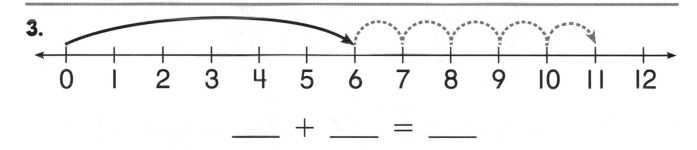

___ + ___ = ___

4.

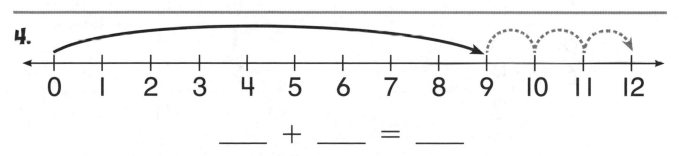

___ + ___ = ___

○ Use with Lesson 2-10, pages 71–72 in the Student Book.
○ Then go to Lesson 2-11, pages 73–74 in the Student Book.

Add: Use Patterns

Name _____

Addition patterns can help you find sums.

Addend	Addend	Sum
3	1	4
4	1	5
5	1	6
6	1	7

Look for a pattern. Fill in the addition chart.

1.

Addend	Addend	Sum
4	0	4
4	1	
4	2	
4	3	

2.

Addend	Addend	Sum
5	2	
4	2	
3	2	
2	2	

3.

Addend	Addend	Sum
4	0	4
5	0	5
6	0	6
	0	7

4.

Addend	Addend	Sum
3	3	
3	2	
3	1	
3		

5.

Addend	Addend	Sum
6	6	
6	5	
6	4	
	3	

6.

Addend	Addend	Sum
0	4	
1	4	
2	4	
	4	

Use with Lesson 2-11, pages 73–74 in the Student Book.
Then go to Lesson 2-12, pages 75–76 in the Student Book.

Doubles

3 addend
+ 3 addend
6 sum

3 + 3 = 6 is a doubles fact.

Write the doubles fact.

1.

___6___ + ___6___ = __12__

2.

___ + ___ = ___

3.

___ + ___ = ___

4.

___ + ___ = ___

5.

___ + ___ = ___

6.

___ + ___ = ___

Find the sum.

7. 5
  + 5

8. 3
  + 3

9. 2
  + 2

10. 1
  + 1

11. 4
  + 4

12. 6
  + 6

C Use with Lesson 2-12, pages 75–76 in the Student Book.
C Then go to Lesson 2-13, pages 77–78 in the Student Book.

twenty-five **25**

Doubles Plus 1

Use a doubles fact to add 1 + 2.

1 + 1 = 2

1 + 2 = 3

1 + 2 is 1 more than 1 + 1.

Find the sum.

1.

3 + 3 = __6__

3 + 4 = ___

2.

5 + 5 = ___

5 + 6 = ___

3.

2 + 2 = ___   2 + 3 = ___

4.

1 + 1 = ___   1 + 2 = ___

5.
$$\begin{array}{r} 4 \\ +4 \\ \hline \end{array} \quad \begin{array}{r} 4 \\ +5 \\ \hline \end{array}$$

6.
$$\begin{array}{r} 1 \\ +1 \\ \hline \end{array} \quad \begin{array}{r} 1 \\ +2 \\ \hline \end{array}$$

7.
$$\begin{array}{r} 2 \\ +2 \\ \hline \end{array} \quad \begin{array}{r} 2 \\ +3 \\ \hline \end{array}$$

8.
$$\begin{array}{r} 3 \\ +3 \\ \hline \end{array} \quad \begin{array}{r} 3 \\ +4 \\ \hline \end{array}$$

9.
$$\begin{array}{r} 0 \\ +0 \\ \hline \end{array} \quad \begin{array}{r} 0 \\ +1 \\ \hline \end{array}$$

10.
$$\begin{array}{r} 5 \\ +5 \\ \hline \end{array} \quad \begin{array}{r} 5 \\ +6 \\ \hline \end{array}$$

Use with Lesson 2-13, pages 77–78 in the Student Book.
Then go to Lesson 2-13A, pages 177–178 in this Workbook and Lessons 2-14 and 2-15, pages 81–84 in the Student Book.

Add Three Numbers

Name _____

To add three numbers, group two addends.
Then add the third addend.

Add down.

$$\begin{array}{r} 2 \\ 4 \\ +3 \end{array} \rightarrow \begin{array}{r} 6 \\ +3 \\ \hline 9 \end{array}$$

Add up.

$$\begin{array}{r} 2 \\ 4 \\ +3 \end{array} \rightarrow \begin{array}{r} 2 \\ +7 \\ \hline 9 \end{array}$$

Add left to right.

$2 + 4 + 3 = ?$

$6 \quad + 3 = 9$

Add right to left.

$2 + 4 + 3 = ?$

$2 + \quad 7 \quad = 9$

Add. You can use [cube] to help.

1. $\begin{array}{r} 5 \\ 3 \\ +3 \end{array} \rightarrow \begin{array}{r} 5 \\ +6 \end{array}$

2. $\begin{array}{r} 3 \\ 1 \\ +8 \end{array} \rightarrow \begin{array}{r} \boxed{} \\ +8 \end{array}$

3. $\begin{array}{r} 2 \\ 2 \\ +5 \end{array} \rightarrow \begin{array}{r} \boxed{} \\ +5 \end{array}$

4. $\begin{array}{r} 1 \\ 1 \\ +9 \end{array} \rightarrow \begin{array}{r} 1 \\ +\boxed{} \end{array}$

5. $\begin{array}{r} 3 \\ 2 \\ +7 \end{array} \rightarrow \begin{array}{r} \boxed{} \\ +7 \end{array}$

6. $\begin{array}{r} 2 \\ 1 \\ +7 \end{array} \rightarrow \begin{array}{r} 2 \\ +\boxed{} \end{array}$

7. $\begin{array}{r} 3 \\ 1 \\ +4 \end{array} \rightarrow \begin{array}{r} 3 \\ +\boxed{} \end{array}$

8. $\begin{array}{r} 3 \\ 4 \\ +4 \end{array} \rightarrow \begin{array}{r} 3 \\ +\boxed{} \end{array}$

9. $2 + 5 + 2 = ?$

$\underline{} + 2 = \underline{}$

10. $2 + 2 + 7 = ?$

$2 + \underline{} = \underline{}$

● Use with Lesson 2-15, pages 83–84 in the Student Book.
● Then go to Lesson 2-16, pages 85–86 in the Student Book.

twenty-seven **27**

Addition Strategies with Three Addends

Name _____

Group doubles.		Count on.
$5 + \boxed{3 + 3} = ?$		$\boxed{5 + 3} + 3 = ?$
$5 + \quad 6 \quad = 11$	Start at 5. Say 6, 7, 8.	$8 \quad + 3 = 11$

Find the sum.
Circle the addends you add first.

1. $\boxed{1 + 1} + 6 = ?$

$\underline{2} + \underline{6} = \underline{8}$

2. $5 + 3 + 2 = ?$

$\underline{} + \underline{} = \underline{}$

3. $7 + 2 + 2 = ?$

$\underline{} + \underline{} = \underline{}$

4. $6 + 2 + 3 = ?$

$\underline{} + \underline{} = \underline{}$

5. $3 + 4 + 2 = ?$

$\underline{} + \underline{} = \underline{}$

6. $3 + 5 + 4 = ?$

$\underline{} + \underline{} = \underline{}$

7. $1 + 1 + 7 = ?$

$\underline{} + \underline{} = \underline{}$

8. $4 + 2 + 4 = ?$

$\underline{} + \underline{} = \underline{}$

9.
$$\begin{array}{r} 5 \\ 1 \\ +5 \\ \hline \end{array} \quad \begin{array}{r} 10 \\ 1 \\ + \\ \hline 11 \end{array}$$

10.
$$\begin{array}{r} 4 \\ 5 \\ +3 \\ \hline \end{array} \quad + \boxed{}$$

11.
$$\begin{array}{r} 8 \\ 1 \\ +1 \\ \hline \end{array} \quad + \boxed{}$$

12.
$$\begin{array}{r} 3 \\ 3 \\ +6 \\ \hline \end{array} \quad + \boxed{}$$

C Use with Lesson 2-16, pages 85–86 in the Student Book.
C Then go to Lesson 2-16A, pages 179–180 in this Workbook.

Problem-Solving Strategy: Write a Number Sentence

Name _____

Read ▶ Archie has 2 .
Millen has 6 more than Archie.
How many does Millen have?

Plan ▶ Write a number sentence.

Write ▶ __2__ + __6__ = __8__
Millen has __8__ .

Check ▶ Change the order of the addends to check.

---

1. Buddy buys 7 .
Phyllis buys 2 more than Buddy. ___ + ___ = ___

   How many does Phyllis buy?   Phyllis buys ___ .

---

2. Vinnie's mom brings 4 to the party.
Steve's dad brings 3 . ___ + ___ = ___

   How many do they bring in all?   They bring ___ .

---

3. Billy picks 2 from his garden. His
sister Del picks 2 more than Billy. ___ + ___ = ___

   How many does Del pick?   Del picks ___ .

---

4. Erma puts 5 in her chili.
Paul puts only 1 in his chili. ___ + ___ = ___

   How many do they use in all?   They use ___ .

☞ Use with Lesson 2-17, pages 87–88 in the Student Book.
☞ Then go to Lesson 2-17A, pages 181–182 in this Workbook.

twenty-nine **29**

Problem-Solving Applications: Mixed Strategies

Name _____

Read ▶ **Plan** ▶ **Write** ▶ **Check**

Use a strategy you have learned.

Strategy File

Act It Out
Draw a Picture
Write a Number Sentence

1. At the zoo, one cage has 2 .
Another cage has 5 .
How many are there in all?

There are __7__ 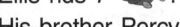.

$2 + 5 = 7$

---

2. Kim sees 6 on a beach.
Two more join them.
How many are there in all?

There are ____ .

---

3. Ellis has 7 .
His brother Percy has 1 .
How many animals do they have in all?

They have ____ animals in all.

---

4. On Monday, Ann sees 3 .
On Tuesday, Todd sees as many as Ann saw.
How many birds do they see in all?

They see ____ birds in all.

---

5. Ray and Dora each catch 2 .
Polly catches 1 .
How many do they catch in all?

They catch ____ in all.

30 thirty

Use with Lesson 2-18, pages 89–90 in the Student Book.

Understanding Subtraction

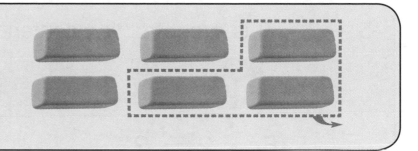

6 in all.

Take away 3 .

3  left.

Use to model each subtraction story.
Write the numbers.

1. __4__ in all.

Take away __1__ .

__3__ left.

2. _____ in all.

Take away _____ .

_____ left.

3. _____ in all.

Take away _____ .

_____ left.

4. _____ in all.

Take away _____ .

_____ left.

C Use with Lesson 3-1, pages 101–102 in the Student Book.
C Then go to Lesson 3-2, pages 103–104 in the Student Book.

Subtraction Sentences

Name _____

5 − 2 = 3 is a subtraction sentence.

5 − 2 = 3

minus equals

A subtraction sentence uses the symbols − and =.

Subtract. Write each subtraction sentence.

1.

_5_ − _3_ = ____

2.

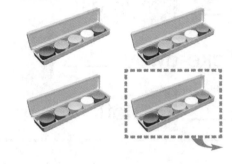

____ − ____ = ____

3.

____ − ____ = ____

4.

____ − ____ = ____

5.

____ − ____ = ____

6.

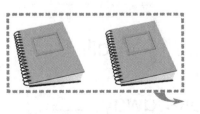

____ − ____ = ____

Use with Lesson 3-2, pages 103–104 in the Student Book.
Then go to Lesson 3-3, pages 105–106 in the Student Book.

Subtract from 6 or Less

Name _____

You can write subtraction facts in two ways.

$$4$$
$$\underline{-\ 1}$$
$$3 \text{ difference}$$

$$4 - 1 = 3$$
$$\text{difference} \leftarrow \boxed{\text{the number left}}$$

Find the difference.

1.
$$6$$
$$\underline{-\ 1}$$
$$5$$
$$6 - 1 = 5$$

2.
$$3$$
$$\underline{-\ 3}$$
$$3 - 3 = \underline{\quad}$$

3.
$$5$$
$$\underline{-\ 1}$$
$$5 - 1 = \underline{\quad}$$

4.
$$3$$
$$\underline{-\ 2}$$
$$3 - 2 = \underline{\quad}$$

5. $4 - 4 = 0$

6. $5 - 0 = \underline{\quad}$

7. $3 - 1 = \underline{\quad}$

8. $6 - 3 = \underline{\quad}$

9. $6 - 5 = \underline{\quad}$

10. $4 - 2 = \underline{\quad}$

11.
$$3$$
$$\underline{-\ 0}$$

12.
$$6$$
$$\underline{-\ 2}$$

13.
$$2$$
$$\underline{-\ 1}$$

14.
$$5$$
$$\underline{-\ 3}$$

15.
$$6$$
$$\underline{-\ 4}$$

16.
$$4$$
$$\underline{-\ 3}$$

© Use with Lesson 3-3, pages 105–106 in the Student Book.
© Then go to Lesson 3-4, pages 107–108 in the Student Book.

All or Zero

Name _____

$$\begin{array}{r} 5 \\ -5 \\ \hline 0 \end{array}$$

$$\begin{array}{r} 5 \\ -0 \\ \hline 5 \end{array}$$

$$\begin{array}{r} 5 \\ +0 \\ \hline 5 \end{array}$$

Add or subtract.

1. $\begin{array}{r} 4 \\ -4 \\ \hline 0 \end{array}$

2. $\begin{array}{r} 3 \\ +0 \\ \hline \end{array}$

3. $\begin{array}{r} 2 \\ -0 \\ \hline \end{array}$

4. $\begin{array}{r} 1 \\ -1 \\ \hline \end{array}$

5. $\begin{array}{r} 6 \\ -0 \\ \hline \end{array}$

6. $\begin{array}{r} 1 \\ +0 \\ \hline \end{array}$

7. $\begin{array}{r} 2 \\ +0 \\ \hline \end{array}$

8. $\begin{array}{r} 4 \\ -0 \\ \hline \end{array}$

9. $\begin{array}{r} 3 \\ -3 \\ \hline \end{array}$

10. $\begin{array}{r} 6 \\ +0 \\ \hline \end{array}$

11. $\begin{array}{r} 4 \\ +0 \\ \hline \end{array}$

12. $\begin{array}{r} 5 \\ +0 \\ \hline \end{array}$

13. $\begin{array}{r} 6 \\ -6 \\ \hline \end{array}$

14. $\begin{array}{r} 0 \\ +5 \\ \hline \end{array}$

15. $\begin{array}{r} 3 \\ -0 \\ \hline \end{array}$

16. $2 - 2 = $ _____

17. $1 - 0 = $ _____

Problem Solving Solve. Use a problem-solving strategy.

18. Jean brought 3 🩹 to the test. None of them got lost. How many 🩹 does she have?

_____ – _____ = _____

19. Cissy has 6 📓 on her desk. She gives them all to Rick. How many 📓 does she have left?

_____ – _____ = _____

C Use with Lesson 3-4, pages 107–108 in the Student Book.
C Then go to Lesson 3-4A, pages 183–184 in this Workbook.

Subtract from 7 and 8

Ed has 7 🍎. Three are red and some are green. How many apples are not red?

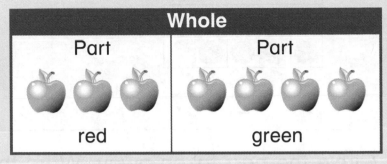

Whole	
Part	Part
🍎 🍎 🍎	🍎 🍎 🍎 🍎
red	green

$$\begin{array}{r} 7 \\ -\,3 \\ \hline 4 \end{array}$$ whole
part
part

$7 \ - \ 3 \ = \ 4$

whole — part = part

4 🍎 are not red.

Subtract.

1.
$$\begin{array}{r} 7 \\ -\,1 \\ \hline 6 \end{array} \qquad \begin{array}{r} 8 \\ -\,4 \\ \hline \end{array} \qquad \begin{array}{r} 7 \\ -\,2 \\ \hline \end{array} \qquad \begin{array}{r} 8 \\ -\,2 \\ \hline \end{array} \qquad \begin{array}{r} 7 \\ -\,4 \\ \hline \end{array} \qquad \begin{array}{r} 8 \\ -\,7 \\ \hline \end{array}$$

2.
$$\begin{array}{r} 8 \\ -\,8 \\ \hline \end{array} \qquad \begin{array}{r} 7 \\ -\,7 \\ \hline \end{array} \qquad \begin{array}{r} 7 \\ -\,5 \\ \hline \end{array} \qquad \begin{array}{r} 8 \\ -\,3 \\ \hline \end{array} \qquad \begin{array}{r} 8 \\ -\,5 \\ \hline \end{array} \qquad \begin{array}{r} 8 \\ -\,0 \\ \hline \end{array}$$

3.
$$\begin{array}{r} 7 \\ -\,3 \\ \hline \end{array} \qquad \begin{array}{r} 8 \\ -\,6 \\ \hline \end{array} \qquad \begin{array}{r} 7 \\ -\,6 \\ \hline \end{array} \qquad \begin{array}{r} 7 \\ -\,0 \\ \hline \end{array} \qquad \begin{array}{r} 8 \\ -\,1 \\ \hline \end{array} \qquad \begin{array}{r} 8 \\ -\,4 \\ \hline \end{array}$$

4.
$7 - 7 = \underline{0} \qquad 7 - 1 = \underline{} \qquad 8 - 5 = \underline{}$

5.
$8 - 4 = \underline{} \qquad 7 - 4 = \underline{} \qquad 7 - 2 = \underline{}$

Ⓒ Use with Lesson 3-5, pages 109–110 in the Student Book.
Ⓒ Then go to Lesson 3-6, pages 111–112 in the Student Book.

Subtract from 9 and 10

Name _____

 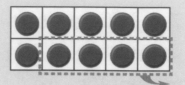

$$9 - 2 = 7 \qquad 10 - 4 = 6$$

Circle the part taken away. Write the difference.

1.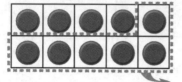

$$10 - 6 = \underline{4}$$

2.

$$10 - 3 = \underline{\quad}$$

3.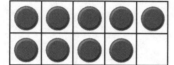

$$9 - 8 = \underline{\quad}$$

4.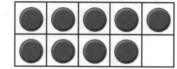

$$9 - 0 = \underline{\quad}$$

Subtract. Use a ▦ and ● to help.

5.
$$\begin{array}{r} 9 \\ -4 \\ \hline 5 \end{array} \qquad \begin{array}{r} 10 \\ -5 \\ \hline \end{array} \qquad \begin{array}{r} 9 \\ -1 \\ \hline \end{array} \qquad \begin{array}{r} 10 \\ -7 \\ \hline \end{array} \qquad \begin{array}{r} 9 \\ -3 \\ \hline \end{array} \qquad \begin{array}{r} 10 \\ -8 \\ \hline \end{array}$$

6.
$$\begin{array}{r} 10 \\ -6 \\ \hline \end{array} \qquad \begin{array}{r} 9 \\ -6 \\ \hline \end{array} \qquad \begin{array}{r} 10 \\ -1 \\ \hline \end{array} \qquad \begin{array}{r} 9 \\ -2 \\ \hline \end{array} \qquad \begin{array}{r} 10 \\ -0 \\ \hline \end{array} \qquad \begin{array}{r} 9 \\ -5 \\ \hline \end{array}$$

7.
$$\begin{array}{r} 10 \\ -9 \\ \hline \end{array} \qquad \begin{array}{r} 9 \\ -7 \\ \hline \end{array} \qquad \begin{array}{r} 10 \\ -10 \\ \hline \end{array} \qquad \begin{array}{r} 10 \\ -2 \\ \hline \end{array} \qquad \begin{array}{r} 9 \\ -0 \\ \hline \end{array} \qquad \begin{array}{r} 9 \\ -9 \\ \hline \end{array}$$

Use with Lesson 3-6, pages 111–112 in the Student Book.
Then go to Lesson 3-7, pages 113–114 in the Student Book.

Subtract from 11 and 12

Name _____

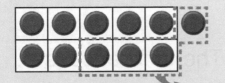   

$$11 - 4 = 7$$ $$12 - 4 = 8$$

Write the difference.

1.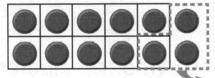

$$12 - 3 = \underline{9}$$

2.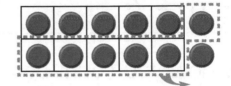

$$12 - 6 = \underline{}$$

Subtract. Use a ⊞ and ● to help.

3.
$$\begin{array}{r} 12 \\ -5 \\ \hline 7 \end{array} \qquad \begin{array}{r} 11 \\ -4 \\ \hline \end{array} \qquad \begin{array}{r} 11 \\ -7 \\ \hline \end{array} \qquad \begin{array}{r} 11 \\ -5 \\ \hline \end{array} \qquad \begin{array}{r} 12 \\ -8 \\ \hline \end{array} \qquad \begin{array}{r} 11 \\ -6 \\ \hline \end{array}$$

4.
$$\begin{array}{r} 12 \\ -9 \\ \hline \end{array} \qquad \begin{array}{r} 12 \\ -7 \\ \hline \end{array} \qquad \begin{array}{r} 11 \\ -2 \\ \hline \end{array} \qquad \begin{array}{r} 11 \\ -8 \\ \hline \end{array} \qquad \begin{array}{r} 11 \\ -3 \\ \hline \end{array} \qquad \begin{array}{r} 12 \\ -6 \\ \hline \end{array}$$

5.
$$\begin{array}{r} 12 \\ -3 \\ \hline \end{array} \qquad \begin{array}{r} 11 \\ -3 \\ \hline \end{array} \qquad \begin{array}{r} 11 \\ -5 \\ \hline \end{array} \qquad \begin{array}{r} 12 \\ -8 \\ \hline \end{array} \qquad \begin{array}{r} 11 \\ -4 \\ \hline \end{array} \qquad \begin{array}{r} 12 \\ -5 \\ \hline \end{array}$$

6.
$$\begin{array}{r} 11 \\ -9 \\ \hline \end{array} \qquad \begin{array}{r} 12 \\ -4 \\ \hline \end{array} \qquad \begin{array}{r} 11 \\ -7 \\ \hline \end{array} \qquad \begin{array}{r} 12 \\ -6 \\ \hline \end{array} \qquad \begin{array}{r} 11 \\ -6 \\ \hline \end{array} \qquad \begin{array}{r} 11 \\ -3 \\ \hline \end{array}$$

Use with Lesson 3-7, pages 113–114 in the Student Book.
Then go to Lesson 3-8, pages 117–118 in the Student Book.

thirty-seven **37**

Number-Line Subtraction

Name _____

$12 - 6 = ?$

| Go to 12. | Count back 6. | The difference is 6. |

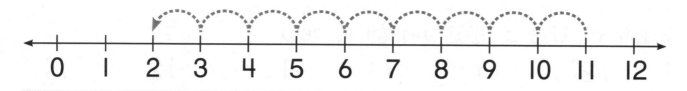

$12 - 6 = 6$

Show how you count back to subtract. Write the difference.

1. $11 - 9 = \underline{2}$

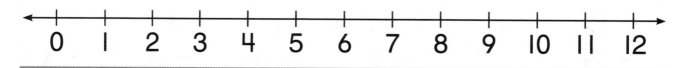

2. $12 - 3 = \underline{}$

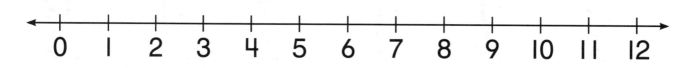

3. $11 - 3 = \underline{}$

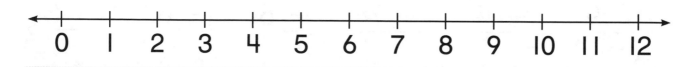

4. $8 - 6 = \underline{}$

C Use with Lesson 3-8, pages 117–118 in the Student Book.
C Then go to Lesson 3-9, pages 119–120 in the Student Book.

Rules and Patterns

Name _____

Whole	Part Taken Away	Part Left
12	5	7
11	5	6
10	5	5

What is the pattern rule?

12 − 5 = 7
11 − 5 = 6
10 − 5 = 5

The pattern rule is − 5.

Fill in the subtraction chart. What is the pattern rule?

1.

Whole	Part Taken Away	Part Left
9	6	
8	6	
7	6	

The pattern rule is _____.

2.

Whole	Part Taken Away	Part Left
6	3	
7	3	
8	3	

The pattern rule is _____.

3.

Whole	Part Taken Away	Part Left
8	7	
9	7	
10	7	

The pattern rule is _____.

4.

Whole	Part Taken Away	Part Left
7	2	
6	2	
5	2	

The pattern rule is _____.

5.

Whole	Part Taken Away	Part Left
4	1	
3	1	
2	1	

The pattern rule is _____.

6.

Whole	Part Taken Away	Part Left
8	0	
7	0	
6	0	

The pattern rule is _____.

Use with Lesson 3-9, pages 119–120 in the Student Book.
Then go to Lesson 3-10, pages 121–122 in the Student Book.

Related Subtraction Facts

Related subtraction facts have the same numbers.
They can be written two ways.

Horizontal	Vertical

$7 - 3 = 4$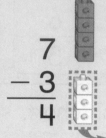

$7 - 4 = 3$

$$\begin{array}{r} 7 \\ -\,3 \\ \hline 4 \end{array}$$

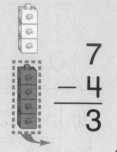

$$\begin{array}{r} 7 \\ -\,4 \\ \hline 3 \end{array}$$

Subtract. Write the related subtraction fact.

1.
$$\begin{array}{r} 5 \\ -\,1 \\ \hline 4 \end{array} \quad \begin{array}{r} 5 \\ -\,4 \\ \hline 1 \end{array}$$

2.
$$\begin{array}{r} 11 \\ -\,6 \\ \hline \end{array} \quad - \,\square$$

3.
$$\begin{array}{r} 9 \\ -\,5 \\ \hline \end{array} \quad - \,\square$$

4.
$$\begin{array}{r} 10 \\ -\,4 \\ \hline \end{array} \quad - \,\square$$

5.
$$\begin{array}{r} 12 \\ -\,3 \\ \hline \end{array} \quad - \,\square$$

6.
$$\begin{array}{r} 7 \\ -\,0 \\ \hline \end{array} \quad - \,\square$$

7.
$$\begin{array}{r} 3 \\ -\,2 \\ \hline \end{array} \quad - \,\square$$

8.
$$\begin{array}{r} 11 \\ -\,7 \\ \hline \end{array} \quad - \,\square$$

9. $8 - 6 = \underline{}$

$\underline{} - \underline{} = \underline{}$

10. $12 - 8 = \underline{}$

$\underline{} - \underline{} = \underline{}$

11. $7 - 5 = \underline{}$

$\underline{} - \underline{} = \underline{}$

12. $11 - 8 = \underline{}$

$\underline{} - \underline{} = \underline{}$

Use with Lesson 3-10, pages 121–122 in the Student Book.
Then go to Lesson 3-11, pages 123–124 in the Student Book.

Relate Addition and Subtraction

These are related addition and subtraction facts.
Both facts use the same numbers.

$$5 + 1 = 6 \qquad 6 - 1 = 5$$

Add. Write the related subtraction fact.

1.
$$2 + 3 = 5$$
$$5 - 3 = 2$$

2.
$$3 + 3 = \underline{\quad}$$
$$\underline{\quad} - \underline{\quad} = \underline{\quad}$$

3.
$$2 + 2 = \underline{\quad}$$
$$\underline{\quad} - \underline{\quad} = \underline{\quad}$$

4.
$$1 + 3 = \underline{\quad}$$
$$\underline{\quad} - \underline{\quad} = \underline{\quad}$$

5.
$$0 + 3 = \underline{\quad}$$
$$\underline{\quad} - \underline{\quad} = \underline{\quad}$$

6.
$$4 + 2 = \underline{\quad}$$
$$\underline{\quad} - \underline{\quad} = \underline{\quad}$$

7.
$$5 + 3 = \underline{\quad}$$
$$\underline{\quad} - \underline{\quad} = \underline{\quad}$$

8.
$$6 + 3 = \underline{\quad}$$
$$\underline{\quad} - \underline{\quad} = \underline{\quad}$$

9.
$$3 + 4 = \underline{\quad}$$
$$\underline{\quad} - \underline{\quad} = \underline{\quad}$$

10.
$$5 + 4 = \underline{\quad}$$
$$\underline{\quad} - \underline{\quad} = \underline{\quad}$$

C Use with Lesson 3-11, pages 123–124 in the Student Book.
C Then go to Lesson 3-11A, pages 185–186 in this Workbook.

Check by Adding

Name _____

Subtract.	Add the parts to check.
$6 - 3 = 3$	$3 + 3 = 6$

Subtract. Then add to check your answer.

1.
$$7 - 2 = 5$$
$$5 + 2 = 7$$

2.
$$11 - 6 = \underline{}$$
$$\underline{} + \underline{} = \underline{}$$

3.
$$8 - 4 = \underline{}$$
$$\underline{} + \underline{} = \underline{}$$

4.
$$9 - 3 = \underline{}$$
$$\underline{} + \underline{} = \underline{}$$

5.
$$\begin{array}{r} 10 \\ -\ 4 \\ \hline 6 \end{array} \quad + \begin{array}{r} 6 \\ 4 \\ \hline \end{array}$$

6.
$$\begin{array}{r} 11 \\ -\ 4 \\ \hline \end{array} \quad + \square$$

7.
$$\begin{array}{r} 12 \\ -\ 4 \\ \hline \end{array} \quad + \square$$

8.
$$\begin{array}{r} 11 \\ -\ 8 \\ \hline \end{array} \quad + \square$$

9.
$$\begin{array}{r} 12 \\ -\ 7 \\ \hline \end{array} \quad + \square$$

10.
$$\begin{array}{r} 10 \\ -\ 8 \\ \hline \end{array} \quad + \square$$

11.
$$\begin{array}{r} 9 \\ -\ 5 \\ \hline \end{array} \quad + \square$$

12.
$$\begin{array}{r} 10 \\ -\ 7 \\ \hline \end{array} \quad + \square$$

13.
$$\begin{array}{r} 12 \\ -\ 6 \\ \hline \end{array} \quad + \square$$

C Use with Lesson 3-12, pages 125–126 in the Student Book.
C Then go to Lesson 3-12A, pages 187–188 in this Workbook.

Fact Families

Name _____

A fact family shows all the related facts for a set of numbers. This is the fact family for 3, 4, 7.

$4 + 3 = 7$ | $3 + 4 = 7$ | $7 - 3 = 4$ | $7 - 4 = 3$

Write the fact families.

1.

$2 + 4 = 6$

___ + ___ = ___

___ − ___ = ___

___ − ___ = ___

2.

$3 + 5 =$ ___

___ + ___ = ___

___ − ___ = ___

___ − ___ = ___

3.

$\begin{array}{r} 3 \\ + 8 \\ \hline \end{array}$ +☐ −☐ −☐

4.

$\begin{array}{r} 5 \\ + 7 \\ \hline \end{array}$ +☐ −☐ −☐

5.

$\begin{array}{r} 6 \\ + 3 \\ \hline \end{array}$ +☐ −☐ −☐

6.

$\begin{array}{r} 2 \\ + 6 \\ \hline \end{array}$ +☐ −☐ −☐

☾ Use with Lesson 3-13, pages 127–128 in the Student Book.
☾ Then go to Lesson 3-14, pages 131–132 in the Student Book.

forty-three **43**

Find Missing Addends

Name _____

Use a subtraction fact to find the missing addend.

$$3 + ? = 6$$
$$6 - 3 = 3$$

The missing addend is 3.

So $3 + 3 = 6$.

Use a subtraction fact to find the missing addend.

1.
$$7 + ? = 11$$
$$\underline{11} - \underline{7} = \underline{4}$$
So $7 + \underline{4} = 11$.

2.
$$8 + ? = 10$$
$$\underline{\quad} - \underline{\quad} = \underline{\quad}$$
So $8 + \underline{\quad} = 10$.

3.
$$? + 6 = 6$$
$$\underline{\quad} - \underline{\quad} = \underline{\quad}$$
So $\underline{\quad} + 6 = 6$.

4.
$$5 + ? = 12$$
$$\underline{\quad} - \underline{\quad} = \underline{\quad}$$
So $5 + \underline{\quad} = 12$.

5.
$$3 + ? = 8$$
$$\underline{\quad} - \underline{\quad} = \underline{\quad}$$
So $3 + \underline{\quad} = 8$.

6.
$$2 + ? = 11$$
$$\underline{\quad} - \underline{\quad} = \underline{\quad}$$
So $2 + \underline{\quad} = 11$.

7.
$$? + 2 = 9$$
$$\underline{\quad} - \underline{\quad} = \underline{\quad}$$
So $\underline{\quad} + 2 = 9$.

8.

$$\begin{array}{r} ? \\ + 3 \\ \hline 4 \end{array} \qquad \begin{array}{r} 4 \\ - 3 \\ \hline \end{array} \qquad \begin{array}{r} \\ + 3 \\ \hline 4 \end{array}$$

9.

$$\begin{array}{r} 6 \\ + ? \\ \hline 10 \end{array} \qquad \begin{array}{r} \\ - \\ \hline \end{array} \qquad \begin{array}{r} 6 \\ + \\ \hline 10 \end{array}$$

Use with Lesson 3-14, pages 131–132 in the Student Book.
Then go to Lesson 3-15, pages 133–134 in the Student Book.

Subtract to Compare

Draw ○ to compare. Then subtract to find the answer.

Rose has 9 .
Joy has 6 .
Who has more?
How many more?

| Rose | ○○○○○○○○○ |
| Joy | ○○○○○○ |

$9 - 6 = 3$

Rose has 3 more .

Draw ○ to compare. Then subtract.

1. Alex bought 4 .
   Tia bought 8 .
   Who bought
   fewer ?
   How many fewer?

| Alex | ○○○○ |
| Tia | ○○○○○○○○ |

$8 - 4 = 4$

Alex bought 4 fewer .

2. Ron has 4 .
   Tom has 7 .
   Who has
   more ?
   How many more?

| Ron | |
| Tom | |

___ − ___ = ___

_____ has ___ more .

3. Ted holds 6 .
   Bryan holds 10 .
   Who holds
   more ?
   How many more?

| Ted | |
| Bryan | |

___ − ___ = ___

_____ holds ___ more .

Use with Lesson 3-15, pages 133–134 in the Student Book.
Then go to Lessons 3-16, 3-17, and 3-18 pages 135–140 in the Student Book.
forty-five 45

Problem-Solving Strategy: Choose the Operation

Name _____

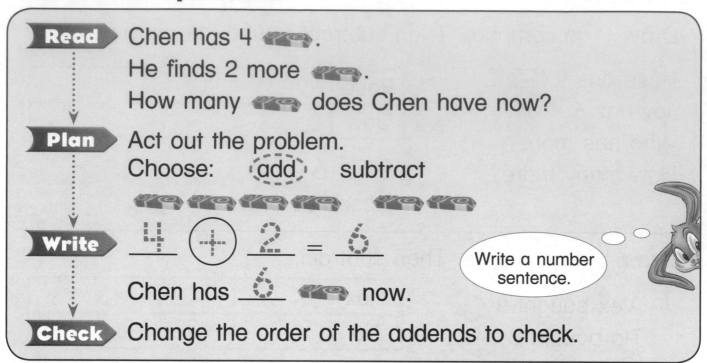

Read Chen has 4 🍥.
He finds 2 more 🍥.
How many 🍥 does Chen have now?

Plan Act out the problem.
Choose: (add) subtract

Write $\underline{4}$ $\oplus$ $\underline{2}$ = $\underline{6}$

Chen has $\underline{6}$ 🍥 now.

Write a number sentence.

Check Change the order of the addends to check.

---

1. Paul has 7 ✏.
He gives 3 ✏ away.
How many ✏ does Paul have now?

add   subtract

____ ◯ ____ = ____

Paul has ____ ✏ now.

2. 6 🖍 are on Tai's desk.
Tai puts 3 more 🖍 there.
How many 🖍 are on Tai's desk then?

add   subtract

____ ◯ ____ = ____

____ 🖍 are on Tai's desk.

---

3. John finds 1 ✒ in his desk and 5 ✒ on the floor.
How many ✒ does John find in all?

add   subtract

____ ◯ ____ = ____

John finds ____ ✒.

4. Alma sees 9 🚩.
5 🚩 are taken away.
How many 🚩 are left?

add   subtract

____ ◯ ____ = ____

There are ____ 🚩 left.

Use with Lesson 3-18, pages 139–140 in the Student Book.
Then go to Lesson 3-19, pages 141–142 in the Student Book.

Problem-Solving Applications: Mixed Strategies

Name _____

Read ▶ **Plan** ▶ **Write** ▶ **Check**

Use a strategy you have learned.

I. Lisa ate 3 yesterday.
She ate 4 today.
How many did Lisa eat in all?

Lisa ate __7__ in all. $3 + 4 = 7$

2. There are 9 on the closet shelf.
4 fall off the shelf.
How many are left?

There are _____ left.

3. Sandy wants to find 10 .
She found 8  yesterday.
How many more does she need to find?

Sandy needs to find _____ more .

4. Ben and Paula each buy 5 📓.
Karen buys 2 📓.
How many 📓 do they buy in all?

They buy _____ 📓 in all.

5. Josie is third in line in the lunch room.
Her friend Eva is 2 children behind Josie.
What position is Eva in line?

Eva is _____ in line.

C Use with Lesson 3-19, pages 141–142 in the Student Book.

Venn Diagrams

Name _____

You can use a Venn diagram to show how things are different and how they are alike.

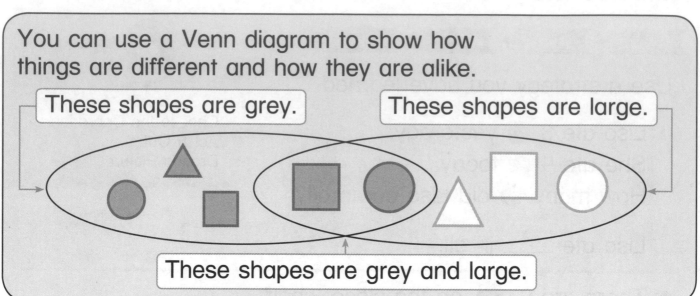

These shapes are grey.

These shapes are large.

These shapes are grey and large.

Draw each shape inside the Venn diagram.

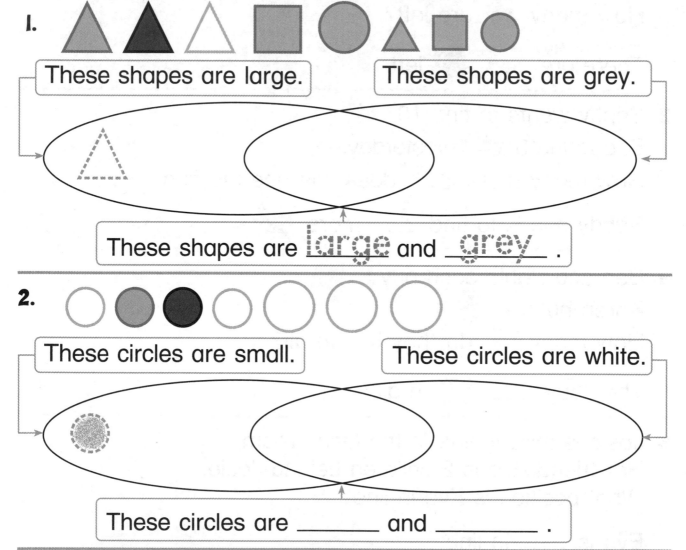

1.

These shapes are large.

These shapes are grey.

These shapes are large and grey .

2.

These circles are small.

These circles are white.

These circles are _____ and _____ .

Use with Lesson 4-1, pages 157–158 in the Student Book.
Then go to Lesson 4-2, pages 159–160 in the Student Book.

Tally Charts

Name _____

Tally the stickers.
Each | stands for 1.
Each |||| stands for 5.

Number of Stickers		
Sticker	Tally	Number
						5
					3
				2

Tally to show how many of each toy dinosaur.
✗ each dinosaur as you make each tally.

1.

Toy Dinosaurs		
Dinosaur	Tally	Number

2. How many dinosaurs did you tally in all?

____ ◯ ____ ◯ ____ = ____

3. How many more 🦖
   than 🦕 did you tally?

____ ◯ ____ = ____

☾ Use with Lesson 4-2, pages 159–160 in the Student Book.
☾ Then go to Lessons 4-3 and 4-4, pages 161–164 in the Student Book.

forty-nine **49**

Picture Graphs

Name _____

Make a picture graph. Draw and color one picture for each shape.

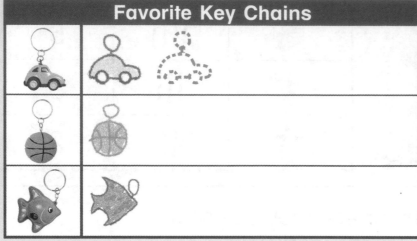

Favorite Key Chains		

Use the picture graph above.

1. Which key chain was the favorite of the fewest children? Circle it.

2. Which key chain was the favorite of the most children? Circle it.

3. How many more children like than ?

____ ◯ ____ = ____   ____ more

4. How many more children like than ?

____ ◯ ____ = ____   ____ more

5. How many fewer children like than ?

____ ◯ ____ = ____   ____ fewer

Ⅽ Use with Lesson 4-4, pages 163–164 in the Student Book.
Ⅽ Then go to Lesson 4-5, pages 165–166 in the Student Book.

Pictographs

Name _____

A pictograph uses a symbol to show how many.

Draw 1 for each tally mark to complete the pictograph.

Mia's Toy Collection	
Toy	Tally
	|||
	̶H̶H̶T̶
	||||

Mia's Toy Collection	
	☺ ☺ ☺
(octopus)	
(fish)	
Key : Each ☺ stands for 1 toy.	

Use the pictograph above.

1. Which animal does Mia have the most of? Circle it.

2. Which animal does Mia have the fewest of? Circle it.

3. How many more 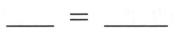 than does Mia have?

____ ◯ ____ = _____   _____ more

4. How many toys does Mia have altogether?

____ ◯ ____ ◯ ____ = _____   _____ toys

Use with Lesson 4-5, pages 165–166 in the Student Book.
Then go to Lesson 4-6, pages 167–168 in the Student Book.

fifty-one **51**

Bar Graphs

Name _____

A bar graph uses bars to show how many.
Complete the bar graph from the tally chart.
Color 1 ☐ for each shape.

Shapes in a Picture	
Shape	**Tally**
▬	卌 I
●	III
■	IIIII
▲	卌

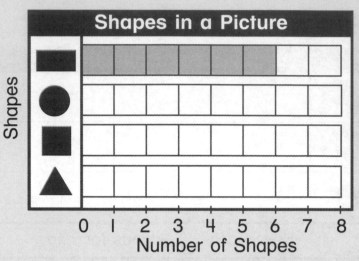

Shapes in a Picture

Shapes

0 1 2 3 4 5 6 7 8
Number of Shapes

Use the bar graph above.

1. How many fewer ▲ are there than ▬?

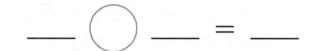
___ ◯ ___ = ___

2. How many more ▲ are there than ●?

___ ◯ ___ = ___

3. How many ▬ and ■ are there in all?

___ ◯ ___ = ___

4. Which shape is there the most of? Circle it.

5. Which shape is there the fewest of? Circle it.

6. How many ▲ and ■ are there in all?

___ ◯ ___ = ___

☞ Use with Lesson 4-6, pages 167–168 in the Student Book.
☞ Then go to Lesson 4-7, pages 171–172 in the Student Book.

Surveys

Name _____

Survey people to collect information, or data, about what they like or think.

Ask 12 friends if they want to go to the river, the ocean, or the lake on their next vacation.

1. Complete the tally chart. Make a tally mark for each answer.

Favorite Vacation Place	
Place	**Tally**
River	
Ocean	
Lake	

2. Use your tally chart to make a bar graph.
Color 1 ☐ for each tally.

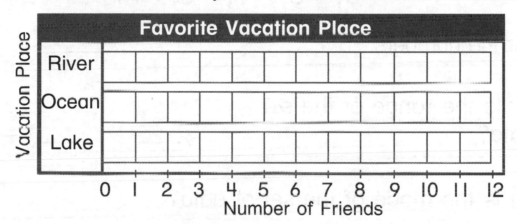

Favorite Vacation Place

Use the bar graph above.

3. Which place do your friends like best? _____

4. Which place do your friends like least? _____

5. How many like the lake or the river best? ____ ◯ ____ = ____

6. How many like the lake or the ocean best? ____ ◯ ____ = ____

Use with Lesson 4-7, pages 171–172 in the Student Book.
Then go to Lesson 4-7A, pages 189–190 in this Workbook.

fifty-three **53**

Range; Mode

Name _____

Order these numbers: 6, 1, 9, 9, 4

(1,) 4, 6, 9, (9)   1, 4, 6, (9,) (9)

↑   ↑
least   greatest

The range is the greatest number minus the least.

$9 - 1 = 8$ ← range

The range is 8.

The mode is the number that you see most often in a set of data.

The mode is 9.

Use the data below to answer questions 1 through 3.

5, 6, 9, 6, 11

1. Order the numbers. _5__, _____, _____, _____, _____

2. What is the range of the set of data?

____ – ____ = ____

3. What is the mode of the set of data? _____

Use the data below to answer questions 4 through 6.

6, 9, 8, 12, 8

4. Order the numbers. _____, _____, _____, _____, _____

5. What is the range of the set of data?

____ – ____ = ____

6. What is the mode of the set of data? _____

Use after Lessons 4-8 and 4-9, pages 173–176 in the Student Book.
Then go to Lesson 4-10, pages 177–178 in the Student Book.

Median

The median is the middle number in an ordered set of numbers.

12, 9, 7, 10, 11

To find the median, order the numbers.

7, 9, (10,) 11, 12

The median is 10.

Order the numbers. Circle the median.

1.

George's Stickers	
	7
	12
	8
	3
	3

____, ____, ____, ____, ____

2.

Sandy's Beads	
	3
	6
	11
	7
	2

____, ____, ____, ____, ____

3.

Kate's Ball Collection	
	10
	4
	3
	8
	5

____, ____, ____, ____, ____

4.

Mr. Hoody's Tools	
	2
	4
	3
	8
	5

____, ____, ____, ____, ____

Use with Lesson 4-10, pages 177–178 in the Student Book.
Then go to Lessons 4-11 and 4-12, pages 179–182 in the Student Book.

fifty-five **55**

Problem-Solving Strategy: Use a Graph

Name _____

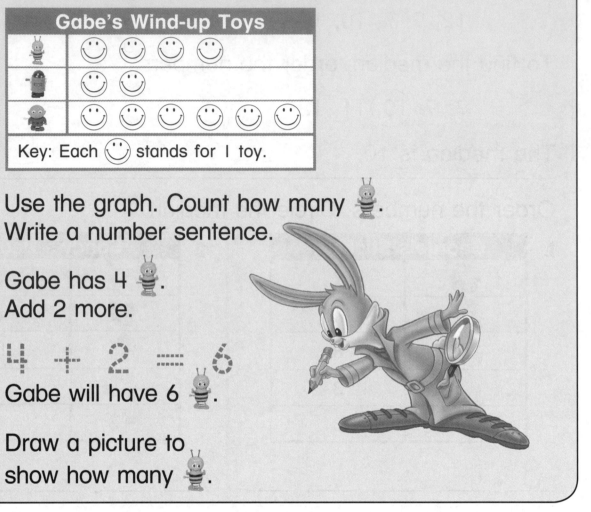

Read If Gabe buys two more 🐝, how many 🐝 will he have?

Gabe's Wind-up Toys

🐝	☺ ☺ ☺ ☺
🤖	☺ ☺
👽	☺ ☺ ☺ ☺ ☺ ☺

Key: Each ☺ stands for 1 toy.

Plan Use the graph. Count how many 🐝. Write a number sentence.

Write Gabe has 4 🐝. Add 2 more.

4 + 2 = 6

Gabe will have 6 🐝.

Check Draw a picture to show how many 🐝.

Use the pictograph above to solve each problem.

1. How many fewer 🤖 than 🐝 does Gabe have?   Gabe has ____ fewer 🤖 than 🐝.

2. If Gabe buys 3 more 🤖, how many 🤖 will he have?   Gabe will have ____ 🤖.

3. How many more 👽 than 🐝 does Gabe have?   Gabe has ____ more 👽 than 🐝.

C Use with Lesson 4-12, pages 181–182 in the Student Book.
C Then go to Lesson 4-13, pages 183–184 in the Student Book.

Problem-Solving Applications: Mixed Strategies

Name _____

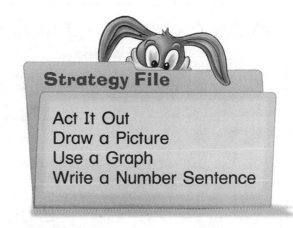

Read ▸ **Plan** ▸ **Write** ▸ **Check**

Use a strategy you have learned.

Books Read During Vacation	
Jonah	✔ ✔ ✔ ✔
Ty	✔ ✔ ✔
Sammy	✔ ✔ ✔ ✔ ✔ ✔
Key: Each ✔ stands for 1 book.	

Strategy File

Act It Out
Draw a Picture
Use a Graph
Write a Number Sentence

Use the graph above for problems 1–3.

1. Who read twice as many books as Ty?
Circle your answer.   Jonah   Sammy

2. How many books in all do Ty and Sammy read?

_____ books in all.

3. How many fewer books does Jonah read than Sammy?

_____ fewer books.

4. Emily has 3 🦀 and 4 🐙.
She also has 3 🦆.
How many stuffed animals does Emily have in all?

Emily has _____ stuffed animals in all.

5. Tim has 8 🚗.
Deb has 3 fewer 🚗 than Tim.
How many 🚗 does Deb have?

Deb has _____ 🚗.

Tens and Ones

Name _____

Make groups of 10 to find how many tens and ones.

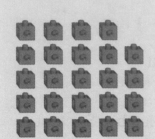

2 groups of 10
and 4 more.

2 tens 4 ones

Circle groups of 10.
Write how many tens and ones.

1.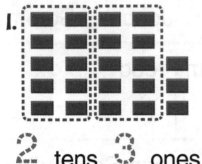

___2___ tens ___3___ ones

2.

_____ tens _____ ones

3.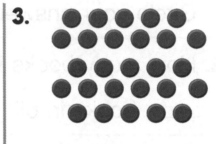

_____ tens _____ ones

4.

_____ ten _____ ones

5.

_____ ten _____ ones

6.

_____ tens _____ ones

7.

_____ tens _____ one

8.

_____ tens _____ ones

9.

_____ ten _____ ones

C Use with Lesson 5-1, pages 195–196 in the Student Book.
C Then go to Lesson 5-2, pages 197–198 in the Student Book.

Tens Through One Hundred

Name _____

You can use models to count by tens.

 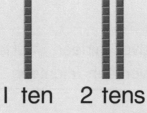 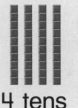 

1 ten	2 tens	3 tens	4 tens	5 tens
10	20	30	40	50
ten	twenty	thirty	forty	fifty

Write how many tens.
Write the number and the number word.

1. 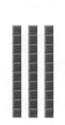 __3__ tens = __30__

thirty

2. 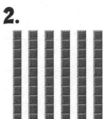 ___ tens = ___

sixty

3. ___ tens = ___

fifty

4. 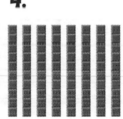 ___ tens = ___

eighty

Write the number.

5. 2 tens = ___

6. 7 tens = ___

7. 3 tens = ___

8. 9 tens = ___

9. 1 ten = ___

10. 6 tens = ___

11. 4 tens = ___

12. 10 tens = ___

13. 9 tens = ___

14. 8 Tens = ___

15. 5 tens = ___

16. 1 ten = ___

C Use with Lesson 5-2, pages 197–198 in the Student Book.
C Then go to Lesson 5-3, pages 199–200 in the Student Book.

Numbers 11 Through 19

Name _____

Thirteen is 1 group of ten and 3 ones.

tens	ones
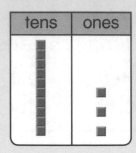	

eleven twelve thirteen fourteen fifteen
sixteen seventeen eighteen nineteen

1 ten 3 ones

13

thirteen

Write the number and the number word.

1.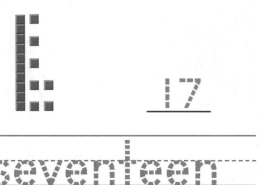

_17_

seventeen

2.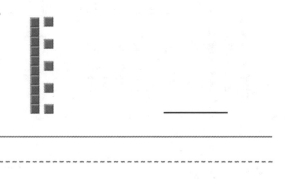

____

_____

Write the number.

3. 1 ten 4 ones _____

4. 1 ten 8 ones _____

5. 1 ten 9 ones _____

6. 1 ten 1 one _____

7. 1 ten 6 ones _____

8. 1 ten 2 ones _____

9. 1 ten 3 ones _____

10. 1 ten 0 ones _____

11. 1 ten 5 ones _____

12. 1 ten 7 ones _____

C Use with Lesson 5-3, pages 199–200 in the Student Book.
C Then go to Lesson 5-4, pages 201–202 in the Student Book.

Numbers
20 Through 39

Name _____

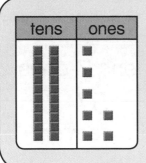 | tens | ones |

2 tens 7 ones
27
twenty-seven

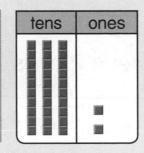 | tens | ones |

3 tens 2 ones
32
thirty-two

Write how many.

1.
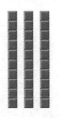

__3__ tens __0__ ones
__30__ thirty

2.
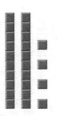

___ tens ___ ones
___ twenty-four

3.

___ tens ___ ones
___ thirty-eight

4.

___ tens ___ ones
___ twenty-five

5.

___ tens ___ one
___ thirty-one

6.

___ tens ___ ones
___ twenty

7.

___ tens ___ ones
___ thirty-six

8.
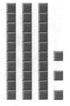

___ tens ___ ones
___ thirty-three

9.

___ tens ___ ones
___ twenty-nine

Ⓒ Use with Lesson 5-4, pages 201–202 in the Student Book.
Ⓒ Then go to Lesson 5-5, pages 203–204 in the Student Book.

Numbers 40 Through 59

Name _____

tens	ones

4 tens 2 ones
42
forty-two

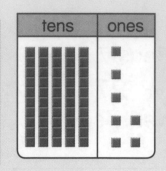

tens	ones

5 tens 7 ones
57
fifty-seven

Write how many.

1.

_5_ tens _1_ one
_51_ fifty-one

2.

___ tens ___ ones
___ forty-eight

3.

___ tens ___ ones
___ forty

4.

___ tens ___ ones
___ fifty-three

5.

___ tens ___ ones
___ forty-four

6.

___ tens ___ ones
___ fifty

7.

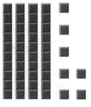

___ tens ___ ones
___ forty-seven

8.

___ tens ___ ones
___ forty-five

9.

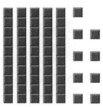

___ tens ___ ones
___ fifty-nine

Use with Lesson 5-5, pages 203–204 in the Student Book.
Then go to Lesson 5-6, pages 205–206 in the Student Book.

Numbers
60 Through 89

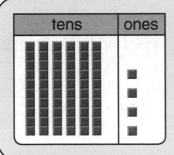 6 tens 4 ones
64
sixty-four

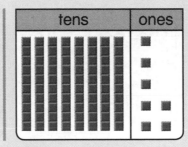 8 tens 7 ones
87
eighty-seven

Write how many.

1.

_7_ tens _6_ ones
_76_ seventy-six

2.

___ tens ___ ones
___ eighty-eight

3.

___ tens ___ ones
___ sixty-three

4.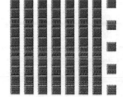

___ tens ___ ones
___ seventy-five

5.

___ tens ___ one
___ sixty-one

6.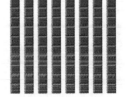

___ tens ___ ones
___ eighty

7.

___ tens ___ ones
___ seventy-eight

8.

___ tens ___ ones
___ eighty-nine

9.

___ tens ___ ones
___ sixty-two

C Use with Lesson 5-6, pages 205–206 in the Student Book.
C Then go to Lesson 5-7, pages 207–208 in the Student Book.

sixty-three **63**

Numbers
90 Through 100

Name _____

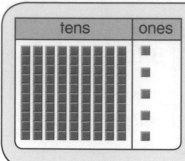 9 tens 5 ones
95
ninety-five

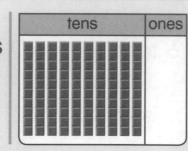 10 tens 0 ones
100
one hundred

Write how many.

1.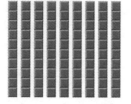

_9_ tens _0_ ones

_90_ ninety

2.

___ tens ___ ones

___ ninety-nine

3.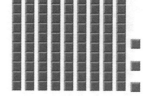

___ tens ___ ones

___ ninety-three

4.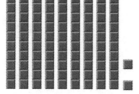

___ tens ___ ones

___ ninety-two

5.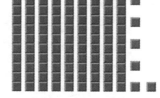

___ tens ___ ones

___ ninety-six

6.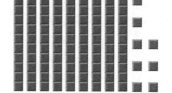

___ tens ___ ones

___ ninety-eight

7.

___ tens ___ one

___ ninety-one

8.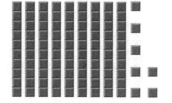

___ tens ___ ones

___ ninety-seven

9.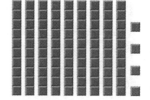

___ tens ___ ones

___ ninety-four

€ Use with Lesson 5-7, pages 207–208 in the Student Book.
€ Then go to Lesson 5-7A, pages 191–192 in this Workbook.

Estimate Quantities

Name _____

Use the 10 🐚 to estimate, or make a good guess, about how many.

10 shells → ⬅ 10 shells

about 20 🐚

about 30 🐚

About how many of each are there?
Circle your estimate.

1.

10 sand dollars

about 20

(about 40)

2.

10 shells

about 20

about 40

3.

10 shells

about 20

about 30

4.

10 shells

about 30

about 40

5.

10 sand dollars

about 20

about 30

6.

10 shells

about 20

about 40

Use with Lesson 5-8, pages 211–212 in the Student Book.
Then go to Lessons 5-9 and 5-10, pages 213–216 in the Student Book.

Place Value of Digits; Expanded Form

38
38 = 3 tens 8 ones
30 + 8 ← [expanded form]

Circle the value of the underlined digit.

1. 6̲7
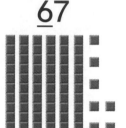
6
(60)

2. 5̲3
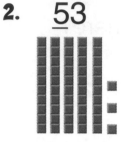
5
50

3. 2̲1̲
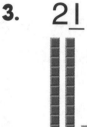
1
10

4. 9̲8̲

8   80

5. 7̲6̲

7   70

6. 1̲9̲

9   90

7. 3̲5̲

3   30

8. 4̲4̲

4   40

9. 8̲2̲

2   20

Write the number for each expanded form.

10. 30 + 4 = _____

11. 90 + 5 = _____

12. 40 + 7 = _____

13. 70 + 8 = _____

14. 80 + 6 = _____

15. 60 + 9 = _____

Use after Lessons 5-9 and 5-10, pages 213–216 in the Student Book.
Then go to Lesson 5-11, pages 217–218 in the Student Book.

One Less, One More   Name _____

Count back 1 to find the number that is one less.	Count on 1 to find the number that is one more.

 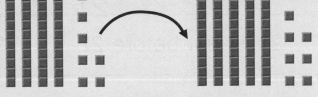

56 is one less than 57.   [57]   58 is one more than 57.

Count on 1.
Write the number that is 1 more.

1. 63, 64	2. 90, ___	3. 29, ___
4. 69, ___	5. 44, ___	6. 72, ___

Count back 1.
Write the number that is 1 less.

7. ___, 80	8. ___, 39	9. ___, 86
10. ___, 90	11. ___, 20	12. ___, 57

Count on or back. Write the number that is
1 less and the number that is 1 more.

13. ___, 96, ___	14. ___, 40, ___	15. ___, 79, ___
16. ___, 71, ___	17. ___, 46, ___	18. ___, 53, ___

C Use with Lesson 5-11, pages 217–218 in the Student Book.
C Then go to Lesson 5-12, pages 219–220 in the Student Book.

sixty-seven **67**

Identify Before, Between, After

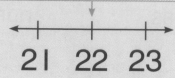

22 is between 21 and 23.

21   22   23

21 is just before 22.   23 is just after 22.

Write the number that comes between.

1.
76 | 77 | 78

2.
34 | ☐ | 36

3.
19 | ☐ | 21

4.
55 | ☐ | 57

5.
41 | ☐ | 43

6.
28 | ☐ | 30

Write the numbers that come just before and just after.

7.
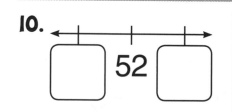
33 | 34 | 35

8.
☐ | 69 | ☐

9.
☐ | 81 | ☐

10.
☐ | 52 | ☐

11.
☐ | 98 | ☐

12.
☐ | 29 | ☐

13.
☐ | 18 | ☐

14.
☐ | 50 | ☐

15.
☐ | 63 | ☐

C Use with Lesson 5-12, pages 219–220 in the Student Book.
C Then go to Lesson 5-13, pages 221–222 in the Student Book.

Compare Numbers

Name _____

Compare 55 and 29.	Compare 63 and 67.	Compare 18 and 18.
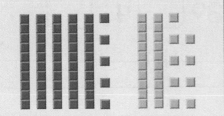	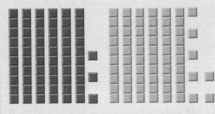	
55 has more tens.	Both have 6 tens.	Both have 1 ten.
	63 has fewer ones.	Both have 8 ones.
55 is greater than 29.	63 is less than 67.	They are equal.
$55 > 29$	$63 < 67$	$18 = 18$

Compare. Write $<$, $=$, or $>$.

1. 21 $<$ 31

2. 47 ◯ 41

3. 22 ◯ 19

4. 56 ◯ 96

5. 74 ◯ 47

6. 44 ◯ 44

7. 81 ◯ 81

8. 29 ◯ 33

9. 65 ◯ 66

10. 63 ◯ 36

11. 58 ◯ 95

12. 98 ◯ 98

Write the numbers to show which is greater or less.

13. 37   73

____ > ____

14. 85   83

____ < ____

15. 51   49

____ > ____

16. 62   26

____ < ____

17. 39   37

____ > ____

18. 44   54

____ < ____

Use with Lesson 5-13, pages 221–222 in the Student Book.
Then go to Lesson 5-14, pages 223–224 in the Student Book.

sixty-nine **69**

Order Numbers

Name _____

A number line can help you put numbers in order.

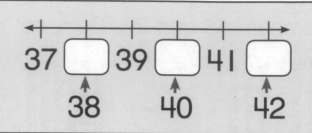

37 ☐ 39 ☐ 41 ☐
38 40 42

Write the missing numbers.

1.

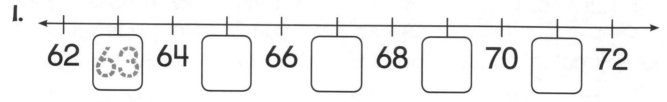

62 **63** 64 ☐ 66 ☐ 68 ☐ 70 ☐ 72

2.

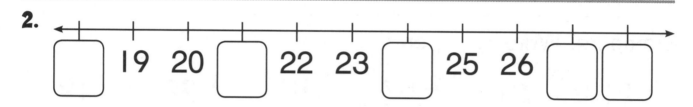

☐ 19 20 ☐ 22 23 ☐ 25 26 ☐ ☐

3.

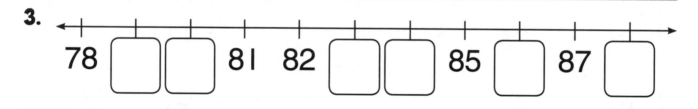

78 ☐ ☐ 81 82 ☐ ☐ 85 ☐ 87 ☐

4.

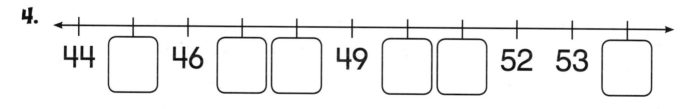

44 ☐ 46 ☐ ☐ 49 ☐ ☐ 52 53 ☐

5.

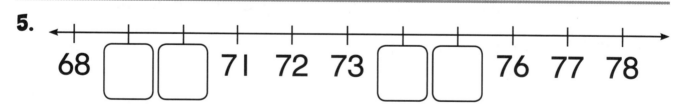

68 ☐ ☐ 71 72 73 ☐ ☐ 76 77 78

6.

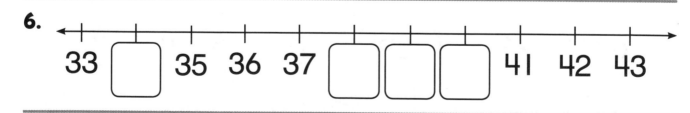

33 ☐ 35 36 37 ☐ ☐ ☐ 41 42 43

C Use with Lesson 5-14, pages 223–224 in the Student Book.
C Then go to Lessons 5-15 and 5-16, pages 225–228 in the Student Book.

Hundred-Chart Patterns;
10 Less, 10 More

Name _____

I. Complete the hundred chart.

1		3		5		7		9	
	12		14		16		18		20
21		23		25		27		29	
	32		34		36		38		40
41		43		45		47		49	
	52		54		56		58		60
61		63		65		67		69	
	72		74		76		78		80
81		83		85		87		89	
	92		94		96		98		100

Write the number that is 10 more or 10 less.

2. 66, _76_

3. 19, ____

4. 50, ____

5. 8, ____

6. 71, ____

7. 34, ____

8. ____, 14

9. ____, 100

10. ____, 53

11. 71, ____

12. 35, ____

13. ____, 42

C Use after Lessons 5-15 and 5-16, pages 225–228 in the Student Book.
Then go to Lessons 5-17 and 5-18, pages 229–234 in the Student Book.

Even and Odd

Name _____

8 is an even number.
None are left over.

7 is an odd number.
One is left over.

Write the number in all. Circle pairs.
Is the number even or odd?

1.

___6___ is ___even___ .

2.

_____ is _____ .

3.

_____ is _____ .

4.

_____ is _____ .

5.

_____ is _____ .

6.

_____ is _____ .

7.

_____ is _____ .

8.

_____ is _____ .

Use with Lesson 5-18, pages 233–234 in the Student Book.
Then go to Lesson 5-19, pages 235–236 in the Student Book.

Count by 5s

I. Count by 5s to complete the hundred chart.

1	2	3	4		6	7	8	9	
11	12	13	14	15	16	17	18	19	20
21	22	23	24		26	27	28	29	30
31	32	33	34	35	36	37	38	39	
41	42	43	44	45	46	47	48	49	50
51	52	53	54		56	57	58	59	60
61	62	63	64	65	66	67	68	69	
71	72	73	74		76	77	78	79	80
81	82	83	84	85	86	87	88	89	90
91	92	93	94		96	97	98	99	

2. Color the count–by–5 numbers on the chart.

Count by 5s. Write the missing numbers.

3. 60, 65, _70_, ____, 80, ____, ____, 95, ____

4. 25, ____, ____, 40, ____, ____, 55, ____, ____

5. ____, 10, ____, ____, 25, ____, 35, ____, ____

Use with Lesson 5-19, pages 235–236 in the Student Book.
Then go to Lesson 5-20, pages 237–238 in the Student Book.

Count by 2s

1. Count by 2s to complete
the hundred chart.

1		3	4	5		7	8	9	
11	12	13		15	16	17		19	20
21		23	24	25		27	28	29	
31	32	33		35	36	37		39	40
41		43		45		47	48	49	
51	52	53	54	55	56	57		59	60
61		63		65	66	67		69	
71	72	73	74	75		77	78	79	80
81		83	84	85	86	87	88	89	90
91	92	93	94	95		97		99	

2. Color the count–by–2 numbers on the chart.

Count by 2s. Write the missing numbers.

3. 70, 72, _74_, ____, ____, ____, ____, 84, ____

4. 55, ____, ____, 61, ____, ____, 67, ____, ____

5. 48, 46, ____, ____, 40, ____, ____, 34, ____

Use with Lesson 5-20, pages 237–238 in the Student Book.
Then go to Lesson 5-21, pages 239–240 in the Student Book.

Problem-Solving Strategy: Logical Reasoning

Name _____

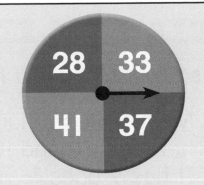

Read ► Ella spins and gets a number.
It is greater than 30.
It is less than 40.
It has 3 ones.
What number does Ella get?

Plan ► Use clues to make a list
to help solve the problem.

Write ► Which numbers on the
spinner are greater than 30?   _33_, _37_, _41_

Which of those numbers
are less than 40?   _33_, _37_

Which of those numbers
has 3 ones?   _33_

Check ► Does your answer match the clues?

---

1. Mark spins and gets a number.
The number is greater than 10.
It is less than 20.
It has 1 one.
What number does Mark get?

Mark gets _____.

---

2. Jules spins and gets a number.
The number is greater than 70.
It is less than 90.
It has no ones in the ones place.
What number does Jules get?

Jules gets _____.

Use with Lesson 5-21, pages 239–240 in the Student Book.
Then go to Lesson 5-22, pages 241–242 in the Student Book.

seventy-five **75**

Problem-Solving Applications: Mixed Strategies

Name _____

Read ❯ **Plan** ❯ **Write** ❯ **Check**

Use a strategy you have learned.

Strategy File

Draw a Picture
Write a Number Sentence
Use Logical Reasoning

1. Marci writes a number
between 30 and 40.
It has 9 ones.
What number does Marci write?

Marci writes _____.

---

2. Paula counts 9 in the store.
She counts a dozen .
How many more than
does Paula count?

Paula counts _____ more .

---

3. Cleon writes three numbers between 6 and 20.
They are 1-digit numbers.
What numbers does Cleon write?

_____, _____, _____

---

4. Ruth has 5 tens 4 ones.
Paul has 10 more than Ruth.
Di has 1 less than Paul.
What numbers do they have?

Ruth _____, Paul _____, Di _____

Use with Lesson 5-22, pages 241–242 in the Student Book.

Sums Through 14

Name _____

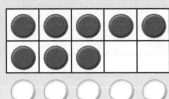 8 + 5 = ?

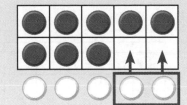 Make 10.

$$8 + 2 = 10$$
$$10 + 3 = 13$$
$$\text{So } 8 + 5 = 13.$$

Add.

1.

$$9 + 5 = \underline{14}$$

2.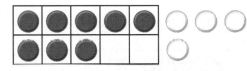

$$8 + 6 = \underline{}$$

3.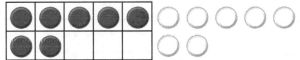

$$7 + 7 = \underline{}$$

4.

$$9 + 4 = \underline{}$$

5.	**6.**	**7.**	**8.**	**9.**
4	5	7	9	8
+ 9	+ 8	+ 7	+ 4	+ 5
13				

10.

$$6 + 7 = \underline{}$$

11.

$$7 + 6 = \underline{}$$

12.

$$5 + 9 = \underline{}$$

13.

$$8 + 6 = \underline{}$$

14.

$$9 + 5 = \underline{}$$

15.

$$5 + 8 = \underline{}$$

Use with Lesson 6-1, pages 257–258 in the Student Book.
Then go to Lesson 6-2, pages 259–260 in the Student Book.

Sums Through 16

$6 + 9 = ?$

Model the addends.

Fill the ten-frame to make 10.

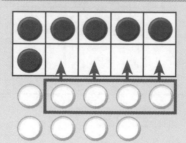

$6 + 4 = 10$

$10 + 5 = 15$

So $6 + 9 = 15$.

Make 10. Then add.

1.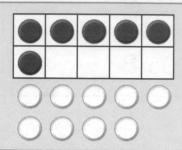

$\begin{array}{r} 9 \\ + 7 \\ \hline 16 \end{array}$

2.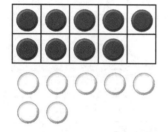

$\begin{array}{r} 7 \\ + 9 \\ \hline \end{array}$

3.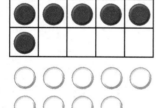

$6 + 9 = \underline{}$

4.

$9 + 6 = \underline{}$

5. $\begin{array}{r} 8 \\ + 8 \\ \hline 16 \end{array}$

6. $\begin{array}{r} 7 \\ + 8 \\ \hline \end{array}$

7. $\begin{array}{r} 8 \\ + 7 \\ \hline \end{array}$

8. $\begin{array}{r} 8 \\ + 5 \\ \hline \end{array}$

9. $\begin{array}{r} 7 \\ + 6 \\ \hline \end{array}$

10. $9 + 7 = \underline{}$

11. $8 + 7 = \underline{}$

12. $6 + 7 = \underline{}$

Use with Lesson 6-2, pages 259–260 in the Student Book.
Then go to Lesson 6-2A, pages 193–194 in this Workbook.

Sums Through 18

$8 + 9 = ?$
$8 + 8 = 16$
$8 + 9$ is 1 more.

So $8 + 9 = 17.$

Make 10 to add.
$9 + 9 = ?$
$9 + 1 = 10$
$10 + 8 = 18$

So $9 + 9 = 18.$

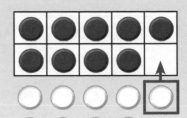

Write the second addend. Then add.

1. $9 + \underline{6} = \underline{15}$

2. $8 + \underline{} = \underline{}$

3. $9 + \underline{} = \underline{}$

4. $9 + \underline{} = \underline{}$

Find the sum.

5.
$\begin{array}{r} 8 \\ + 9 \\ \hline 17 \end{array}$

6.
$\begin{array}{r} 7 \\ + 9 \\ \hline \end{array}$

7.
$\begin{array}{r} 8 \\ + 8 \\ \hline \end{array}$

8.
$\begin{array}{r} 9 \\ + 9 \\ \hline \end{array}$

9.
$\begin{array}{r} 6 \\ + 9 \\ \hline \end{array}$

10.
$\begin{array}{r} 9 \\ + 5 \\ \hline \end{array}$

11. $9 + 7 = \underline{}$

12. $5 + 9 = \underline{}$

13. $8 + 7 = \underline{}$

14. $7 + 7 = \underline{}$

15. $6 + 8 = \underline{}$

16. $9 + 9 = \underline{}$

Use with Lesson 6-3, pages 261–262 in the Student Book.
Then go to Lesson 6-3A, pages 195–196 in this Workbook.

seventy-nine **79**

Subtract from 13 and 14

Name _____

$14 - 6 = ?$

Subtract.	Add to check.
14	8
− 6	+ 6
8	14

$14 - 6 = 8$

Subtract. Add to check.

1.

$13 - 4 = \underline{9}$

___ + ___ = ___

2.

$14 - 9 = $ ___

___ + ___ = ___

3.

$14 - 5 = $ ___

___ + ___ = ___

4.

$13 - 8 = $ ___

___ + ___ = ___

5.

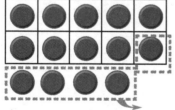

6.
14
− 7   +

7.
14
− 8   +

8. $13 - 5 = $ ___

___ + ___ = ___

9. $13 - 7 = $ ___

___ + ___ = ___

C Use with Lesson 6-5, pages 267–268 in the Student Book.
C Then go to Lesson 6-6, pages 269–270 in the Student Book.

Subtract from 16 or Less

$$16 - 7 = ?$$
$$16 - 7 = 9$$

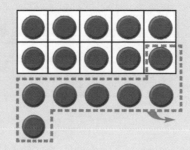

Subtract. Circle the part taken away.

1. 15
  − 9
  6

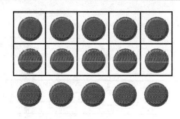

2. 14
  − 9

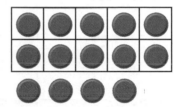

3. 15
  − 7

4. 16
  − 8

5. 16
  − 9

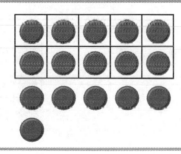

6. 15
  − 6

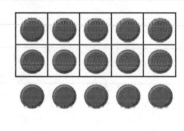

Find the difference. Use ▦ and ● to help.

7. 14 − 7 | **8.** 14 − 6 | **9.** 15 − 8 | **10.** 15 − 7 | **11.** 16 − 9

12.
$$16 - 7 = \underline{\quad}$$

13.
$$16 - 9 = \underline{\quad}$$

14.
$$16 - 8 = \underline{\quad}$$

Use with Lesson 6-6, pages 269–270 in the Student Book.
Then go to Lesson 6-7, pages 271–272 in the Student Book.

eighty-one **81**

Subtract from 18 or Less

Name _____

$$18 - 9 = ?$$

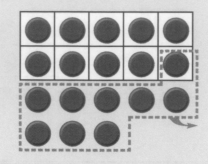

$$18 - 9 = 9$$

Subtract.

1.
$$\begin{array}{r} 15 \\ -\ 6 \\ \hline 9 \end{array}$$

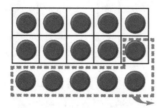

2.
$$\begin{array}{r} 17 \\ -\ 9 \\ \hline \end{array}$$

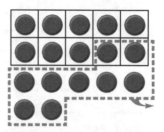

3.
$$\begin{array}{r} 17 \\ -\ 8 \\ \hline \end{array}$$

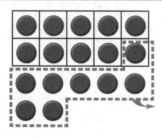

4.
$$\begin{array}{r} 16 \\ -\ 9 \\ \hline \end{array}$$

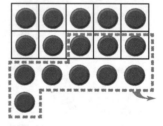

5.
$$\begin{array}{r} 18 \\ -\ 9 \\ \hline \end{array}$$

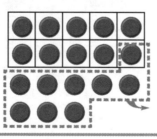

6.
$$\begin{array}{r} 15 \\ -\ 9 \\ \hline \end{array}$$

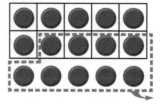

7.
$$\begin{array}{r} 16 \\ -\ 8 \\ \hline 8 \end{array}$$

8.
$$\begin{array}{r} 17 \\ -\ 9 \\ \hline \end{array}$$

9.
$$\begin{array}{r} 16 \\ -\ 7 \\ \hline \end{array}$$

10.
$$\begin{array}{r} 15 \\ -\ 8 \\ \hline \end{array}$$

11. $17 - 8 = $ ___

12. $16 - 9 = $ ___

13. $15 - 7 = $ ___

C Use with Lesson 6-7, pages 271–272 in the Student Book.
C Then go to Lesson 6-7A, pages 197–198 in this Workbook.

More Fact Families

Name _____

A fact family shows all the related facts.

7	4	11
+	−	=

7	+	4	=	11
4	+	7	=	11
11	−	4	=	7
11	−	7	=	4

Write each fact family.

1. 15   6   9

6 9 = 15

   = ___

 ___ = ___

___ ___ = ___

2. 16   7   9

7 ◯ 9 = ___

___ ◯ ___ = ___

___ ◯ ___ = ___

___ ◯ ___ = ___

3. 9   18

___ ◯ ___ = ___

___ ◯ ___ = ___

4. 8   16

___ ◯ ___ = ___

___ ◯ ___ = ___

5.

8			
+ 6	◯	◯	◯

14

6.

8			
◯ 9	◯	◯	◯

C Use with Lesson 6-8, pages 273–274 in the Student Book.
C Then go to Lesson 6-9, pages 277–278 in the Student Book.

eighty-three **83**

Copyright © by William H. Sadlier, Inc. All rights reserved.

Three Addends

You can change the order to add.

Add down.	Add up.	Make 10.	Use doubles.
2 7 → 9 + 5 + 5 14	5 3 5 + 4 → + 7 12	7 1 → 10 + 3 + 1 11	3 3 → 6 + 2 + 2 8

Add. Circle the numbers you add first.

I.
```
  6        10
  4      +  2
+ 2      ———
         12
```

2.
```
  3       □
  6      +□
+ 4      ——
```

3.
```
  2       □
  7      +□
+ 5      ——
```

4.
```
  7       □
  3      +□
+ 4      ——
```

5.
```
  3       □
  3      +□
+ 6      ——
```

6.
```
  1       □
  8      +□
+ 2      ——
```

7.
```
  6       □
  3      +□
+ 2      ——
```

8.
```
  9       □
  3      +□
+ 0      ——
```

9.
```
  5       □
  4      +□
+ 4      ——
```

10.

$7 + 0 + 8 = \ ?$

___ + ___ = ___

II.

$4 + 5 + 1 = \ ?$

___ + ___ = ___

C Use with Lesson 6-9, pages 277–278 in the Student Book.
C Then go to Lesson 6-10, pages 279–280 in the Student Book.

Extending Facts to 20

9 + 10 = ?	20 − 10 = ?
Use a doubles fact. 9 + 9 = 18 10 is one more than 9. So 9 + 10 = 19.	 Take away 10. 20 − 10 = 10

Add or subtract.

1. 9 + 9 = 18

2. 8 + 7 = ___

3. 9 + 8 = ___

4. 10 + 9 = ___

5. 19 − 9 = ___

6. 8 + 9 = ___

7. 20 − 10 = ___

8. 15 − 9 = ___

9. 7 + 9 = ___

10. 17 − 9 = ___

11. 16 − 7 = ___

12. 8 + 8 = ___

13.
$$\begin{array}{r} 18 \\ -\ 9 \\ \hline 9 \end{array}$$

14.
$$\begin{array}{r} 17 \\ -\ 8 \\ \hline \end{array}$$

15.
$$\begin{array}{r} 9 \\ +\ 6 \\ \hline \end{array}$$

16.
$$\begin{array}{r} 8 \\ +\ 7 \\ \hline \end{array}$$

17.
$$\begin{array}{r} 20 \\ -10 \\ \hline \end{array}$$

18.
$$\begin{array}{r} 7 \\ +\ 7 \\ \hline \end{array}$$

19.
$$\begin{array}{r} 16 \\ -\ 7 \\ \hline \end{array}$$

20.
$$\begin{array}{r} 10 \\ +10 \\ \hline \end{array}$$

21.
$$\begin{array}{r} 15 \\ -\ 8 \\ \hline \end{array}$$

22.
$$\begin{array}{r} 10 \\ +\ 9 \\ \hline \end{array}$$

Use with Lesson 6-10, pages 279–280 in the Student Book.
Then go to Lesson 6-10A, pages 199–200 in this Workbook.

Missing Part of a Number Sentence

Name _____

$8 + ? = 12$	Count up.	Use a subtraction fact.
	$8 + ? = 12$	$8 + ? = 12$
	Count up from 8:	$12 - 8 = \ 4$
	9, 10, 11, 12	
	$8 + 4 = 12$	So $8 + 4 = 12.$

What number will make each number sentence true?
Use to help.

1. $7 + \boxed{9} = 16$

2. $8 + \boxed{} = 13$

3. $\boxed{} + 4 = 11$

4. $17 - \boxed{} = 9$

5. $\boxed{} + 10 = 20$

6. $14 - \boxed{} = 5$

7. $6 + \boxed{} = 13$

8. $\boxed{} + 10 = 19$

9. $\boxed{} + 7 = 14$

10. $17 - \boxed{} = 8$

11. $9 + \boxed{} = 12$

12. $\boxed{} - 9 = 9$

13. $11 - \boxed{} = 3$

14. $9 + \boxed{} = 16$

Use with Lesson 6-11, pages 281–282 in the Student Book.
Then go to Lesson 6-11A, pages 201–202 in this Workbook.

Problem-Solving Strategy: Make a Table

Read ▶ Hans found 5 pairs of gloves in his closet.
One pair of gloves fits 10 fingers.
How many fingers fit in 5 pairs of gloves?

Plan ▶ Name the facts you know.
- One pair of gloves fits 10 fingers.
- Hans has 5 pairs of gloves.

Make a table.

Write ▶

Pairs of Gloves	1	2	3	4	5
Fingers	10	20	30	40	50

50 fingers fit in 5 pairs of gloves.

Check ▶ Draw a picture. Did you find 50 fingers in all?

Make a table to solve each problem.

1. Manuel sees 6 bicycles in the store.
Each bicycle has 2 wheels.
How many wheels does Manuel see in all?

Bicycles	1	2	3	4	5	6
Wheels	2	4				

_____ wheels in all.

2. Mr. Hall hands out 5 bags of crackers.
Each bag has 5 crackers in it.
How many crackers does Mr. Hall hand out in all?

Bag	1	2	3	4	5
Crackers					

_____ crackers in all.

Use with Lesson 6-12, pages 283–284 in the Student Book.
Then go to Lesson 6-13, pages 285–286 in the Student Book.

eighty-seven **87**

Problem-Solving Applications: Mixed Strategies

Name _____

Read ▸ **Plan** ▸ **Write** ▸ **Check**

Use a strategy you have learned.

Strategy File
Draw a Picture
Choose the Operation
Make a Table

1. Each has 5 strings.
There are 7 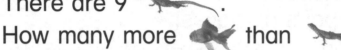.
How many strings are there in all?

There are _____ strings in all.

2. There are 14 in the aquarium.
There are 9 .
How many more than
are in the aquarium?

There are ____ more .

3. June is 7th in line at the garage sale.
Polly is 2nd in line.
How many people are in line
between June and Polly?

____ people are between June and Polly.

4. Jimmy spins and gets a number.
The number is greater than 40.
It is less than 51.
It has 7 ones.
What number does Jimmy get?

Jimmy gets ____.

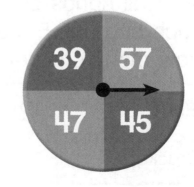

Use with Lesson 6-13, pages 285–286 in the Student Book.

Open and Closed Figures; Sides and Corners

Name _____

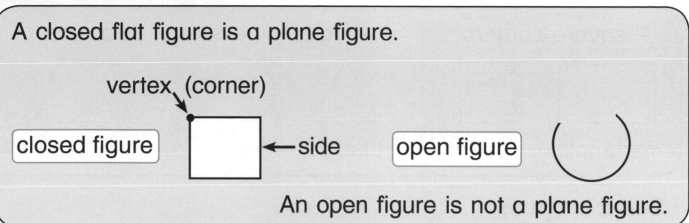

A closed flat figure is a plane figure.

vertex (corner)

closed figure ← side | open figure

An open figure is not a plane figure.

Draw to make each a closed figure.

I.

2.

3.

4.

Trace each figure.
Draw a ● at each vertex.
Write how many sides and corners.

5.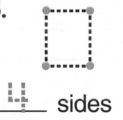

__4__ sides

__4__ corners

6.

_____ sides

_____ corners

7.

_____ sides

_____ corners

8.

_____ sides

_____ corners

9.

_____ sides

_____ corners

10.

_____ sides

_____ corners

II.

_____ sides

_____ corners

12.

_____ sides

_____ corners

Use after Lessons 7-1 and 7-2, pages 297–300 in the Student Book.
Then go to Lesson 7-2A, pages 203–204 in this Workbook.

eighty-nine **89**

Sorting Plane Figures

Name _____

4 square corners	0 square corners	4 corners
rectangle square	triangle circle	trapezoid

Sort the figures.
Circle the figures that follow each rule.

	Rule	Figures
1.	0 corners	
2.	3 corners and 3 sides	
3.	4 square corners and 4 sides	
4.	5 corners and 5 sides	
5.	1 square corner and 3 sides	
6.	4 corners and 4 sides	

Use with Lesson 7-3, pages 301–302 in the Student Book.
Then go to Lesson 7-3A, pages 205–206 in this Workbook.

Ways to Make Figures

Name _____

You can make a plane figure or take apart
a plane figure using different shapes.

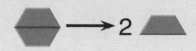

2 △ and 2 ◆ → ⬡ | ⬡ → 2 ▱

Use pattern blocks to make a new figure.
How many of each pattern block did you use?

1. Use △ to make a ▱. | **2.** Use ◆ to make a ⬡.

___3___ △ make I ▱. | _____ ◆ make I ⬡.

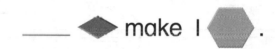

3. Use △ to make a ⬡. | **4.** Use △ to make a ◆.

_____ △ make I ⬡. | _____ △ make I ◆.

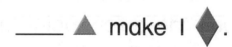

Draw lines to show how to make different shapes.
Use pattern blocks to help.

5. 2 ▱ | **6.** 3 △ | **7.** 6 △

 | 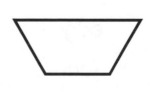 | ⬡

C Use with Lesson 7-4, pages 303–304 in the Student Book.
C Then go to Lessons 7-5 and 7-6, pages 307–310 in the
Student Book and Lesson 7-5A, pages 207–208 in this Workbook.

Solid Figures; Attributes of Solid Figures

Name _____

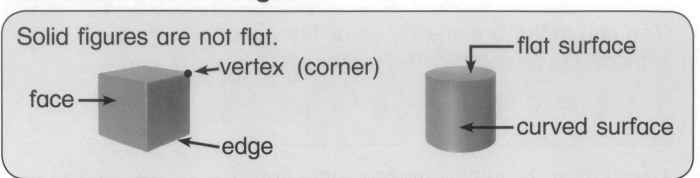

Solid figures are not flat.

face → | vertex (corner)

edge

flat surface

curved surface

Color the figures that have the same shape.

1.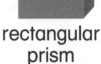
rectangular prism

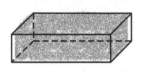

2.
cylinder

  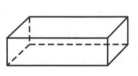

3.
pyramid

 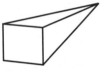 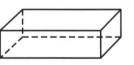

What does the arrow point to?
Circle the correct math word.

4.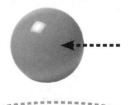

~~curved surface~~

vertex

5.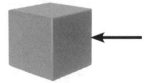

edge

face

6.

curved surface

flat surface

Use after Lessons 7-5 and 7-6, pages 307–310 in the Student Book.
Then go to Lesson 7-7, pages 311–312 in the Student Book.

Plane Figures on Solid Figures

Name _____

The flat surfaces of solid figures are shaped like plane figures.

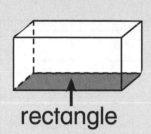 rectangle

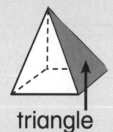 triangle

 circle

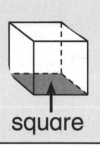 square

Circle any solid figure with a flat surface that matches the plane figure at the beginning of each row.

1.  |

2. |

3. |

Write **square**, **triangle**, or **circle**.

4. The face of a cube is a ____square____.

5. Four faces of a pyramid are _____.

6. Each flat surface of a cylinder is a _____.

7. The flat surface of a cone is a _____.

Use with Lesson 7-7, pages 311–312 in the Student Book.
Then go to Lesson 7-8, pages 313–314 in the Student Book.

ninety-three **93**

Graphing Attributes

Name _____

I. Make a bar graph for each.
Color I box for each side on the plane figures.

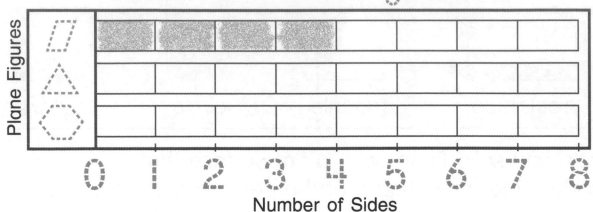

Sides of Plane Figures

2. Color I box for each corner on the solid figures.

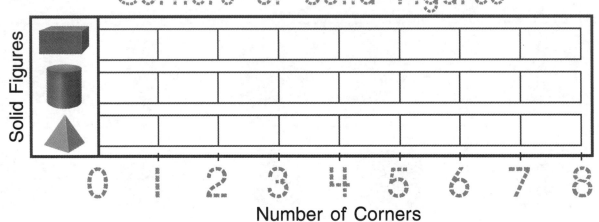

Corners of Solid Figures

3. Color I box for each face on the solid figures.

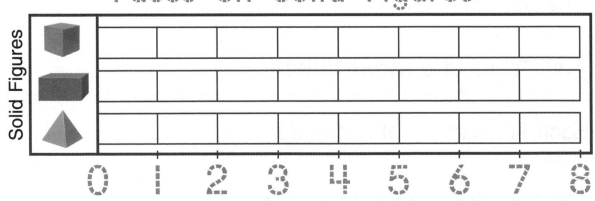

Faces on Solid Figures

Use with Lesson 7-8, pages 313–314 in the Student Book.
Then go to Lesson 7-9, pages 315–316 in the Student Book.

Roll, Slide, and Stack Name _____

Solid figures can move in different ways.

A sphere has a curved surface.	A rectangular prism has a flat surface.	A cylinder has flat surfaces on the top and bottom.
A sphere can roll.	 A rectangular prism can slide.	 A cylinder can stack.

Circle solid figures to show
if they roll, slide, or stack.

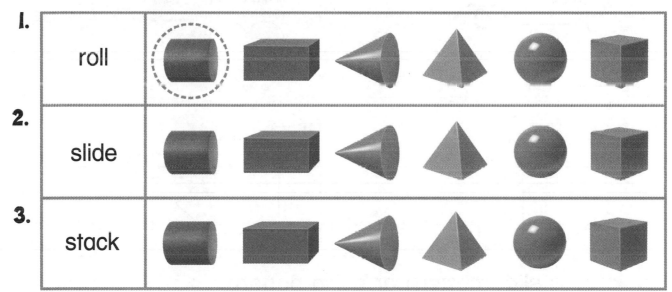

1. roll

2. slide

3. stack

4. Color each solid figure that both rolls and slides.

5. Color each solid figure that both stacks and rolls.

Use with Lesson 7-9, pages 315–316 in the Student Book.
Then go to Lesson 7-10, pages 319–320 in the Student Book.

ninety-five **95**

Slides and Flips

Name _____

Plane figures can move in different ways.

A slide moves a figure along a line.	A flip turns a figure over.

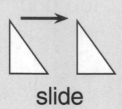

slide

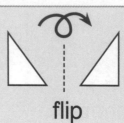

flip

Model each slide or flip.
Trace the shape to show how it was moved.

1. Flip the .

2. Slide the ♡.

3. Slide the 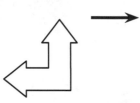.

4. Flip the 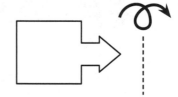.

Look for a slide pattern or a flip pattern.
Draw what is most likely to come next.

5.

_____

6.

_____

Use with Lesson 7-10, pages 319–320 in the Student Book.
Then go to Lesson 7-11, pages 321–322 in the Student Book.

Slides and Turns

Name _____

A figure can slide to the right, left, up, or down. 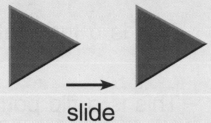 slide	A figure can turn around a point. 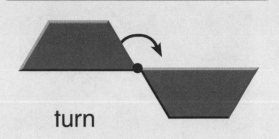 turn

Model each slide or turn.
Trace the shape to show how it was moved.

1. Slide the .

2. Turn the  .

3. Turn the  .

4. Slide the 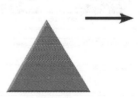 .

Look for a slide pattern or a turn pattern.
Draw what is most likely to come next.

5.

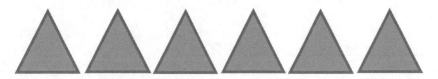

6.

Use with Lesson 7-11, pages 321–322 in the Student Book.
Then go to Lesson 7-12, pages 323–324 in the Student Book.

ninety-seven **97**

Pattern Rules

Name _____

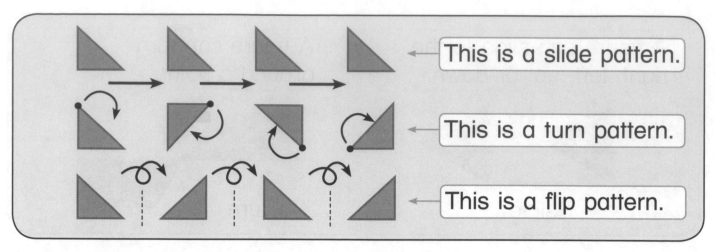

This is a slide pattern.

This is a turn pattern.

This is a flip pattern.

Write **slide**, **turn**, or **flip** to describe each pattern.
Circle what comes next in each pattern.

1.

This is a ___~~slide~~___ pattern.

2.

This is a _____ pattern.

3.

This is a _____ pattern.

4.

This is a _____ pattern.

Use with Lesson 7-12, pages 323–324 in the Student Book.
Then go to Lessons 7-13 and 7-14, pages 327–330 in the Student Book.

Give and Follow Directions

Name _____

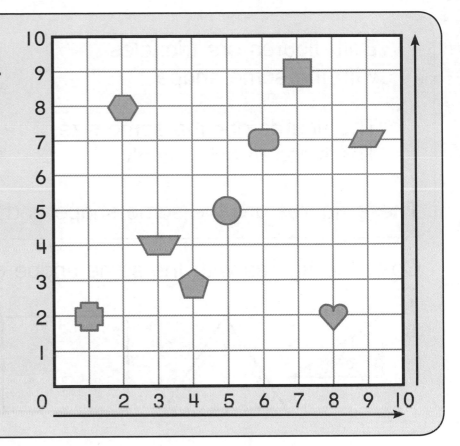

Where is the ▱ ?
To find out, start at 0.

Count across.
Count up.

The ▱ is 9 across
and 7 up.

Use the grid above.
Write the numbers to tell where each figure is.

Figure	Across	Up
1. ⬠	4	3
2. ✚		
3. ♥		
4. ⬡		

Figure	Across	Up
5. ▱		
6. ■		
7. ●		
8. ⬭		

Look at the grid. Circle the correct answer.

9. Is the ● to the right
   or left of the ■?   right   left

10. Is the ● above or below the ⬭?   above   below

Use with Lesson 7-14, pages 329–330 in the Student Book.
Then go to Lesson 7-15, pages 331–332 in the Student Book.

ninety-nine **99**

Same Shape and Size

Name _____

Both figures are triangles with the same shape.

The figures are the same size. The sides match exactly.

These figures are the same shape and the same size.

Color the figures with the same shape and the same size.

1.

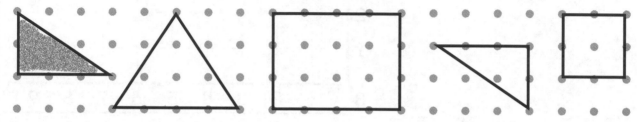

2.

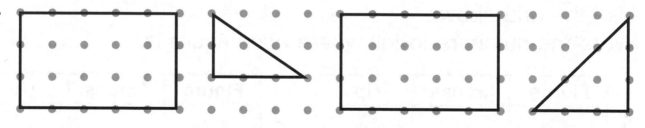

3.

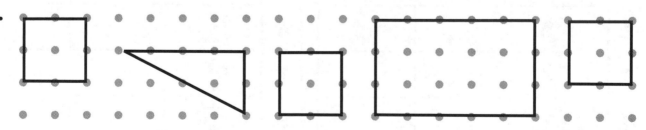

4.

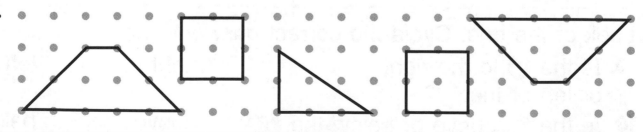

Use with Lesson 7-15, pages 331–332 in the Student Book.
Then go to Lesson 7-16, pages 333–334 in the Student Book.

Symetry

Name _____

Shapes with symmetry have matching parts.

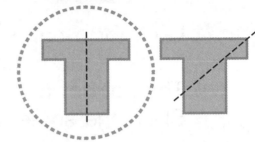

The fold line is the line of symmetry.

Look for a line of symmetry. Circle the shape that shows matching parts.

I.
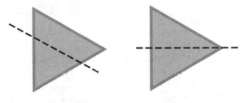

2.
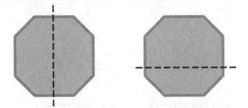

3.

4.
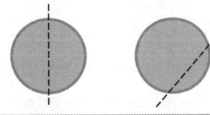

5.
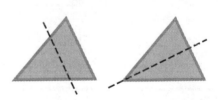

6.
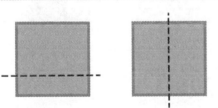

7.
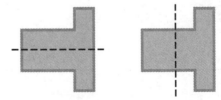

8.
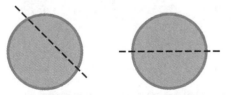

9.
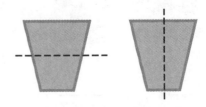

10.
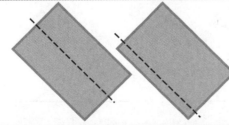

II.

Use with Lesson 7-16, pages 333–334 in the Student Book.
Then go to Lesson 7-17, pages 335–336 in the Student Book.

one hundred one **101**

Problem-Solving Strategy: Find/Use a Pattern

Name _____

Read ▸ How can you show this pattern using numbers?

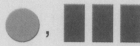 , , ● ,  , ,

Plan ▸ Look for a pattern rule.
Think of the parts that repeat.
The pattern rule is 1 circle, then 3 rectangles.
Show the same pattern with the numbers 1 and 3.

Write ▸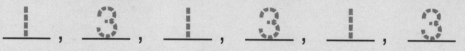

1 , 3 , 1 , 3 , 1 , 3
___ ___ ___ ___ ___ ___

Check ▸ Does your number pattern follow the same rule as the shape pattern?

Find a pattern. Show the same pattern using numbers.

1.

3 , 2 , ___ , ___ , ___ , ___

2. ,  , , , ,

___ , ___ , ___ , ___ , ___ , ___

3.

___ , ___ , ___ , ___ , ___ , ___

Use with Lesson 7-17, pages 335–336 in the Student Book.
Then go to Lesson 7-18, pages 337–338 in the Student Book.

Problem-Solving Applications: Mixed Strategies

Name _____

Read ▶ **Plan** ▶ **Write** ▶ **Check**

Use a strategy you have learned.

1. Bari makes a pattern with these shapes. Show the same pattern using numbers.

 , , , , , , ,

_____ , _____ , _____ , _____ , _____ , _____

2. Bill spins and gets a number.
The number is less than 100.
It is more than 90.
It has 3 ones.
What number does Bill get?

Bill gets _____ .

3. I can slide.
I cannot roll.
I have 6 faces.
What figure am I?
Circle your answer.

4. Dusty spends 8¢ on a .
He pays with a dime.
How much does Dusty have left?

Dusty has _____ left.

Use with Lesson 7-18, pages 337–338 in the Student Book.

Nickels and Pennies

Name _____

Count on by 5s for nickels.
Count on by 1s for pennies.

5¢,   10¢,   15¢,   16¢,   17¢,   18¢

Count on. Write how much.

1.

5¢, 6¢, 7¢, 8¢, 9¢, 10¢

10¢

2.

_____¢, _____¢, _____¢, _____¢, _____¢

_____¢

3.

_____¢, _____¢, _____¢, _____¢

_____¢

4.

_____¢, _____¢, _____¢, _____¢, _____¢, _____¢

_____¢

C Use with Lesson 8-1, pages 353–354 in the Student Book.
C Then go to Lesson 8-2, pages 355–356 in the Student Book.

Dimes and Pennies

Name _____

> | Count on by 10s for dimes. | Count on by 1s for pennies. |
>
>
>
> 10¢,　20¢,　30¢,　31¢,　32¢,　33¢

Count on. Write how much.

1.

10¢, 11¢, 12¢, 13¢, 14¢, 15¢    15¢

2.

____¢, ____¢, ____¢, ____¢, ____¢, ____¢    ____¢

3.

____¢, ____¢, ____¢, ____¢, ____¢, ____¢    ____¢

4.

____¢, ____¢, ____¢, ____¢, ____¢, ____¢    ____¢

Use with Lesson 8-2, pages 355–356 in the Student Book.
Then go to Lesson 8-3, pages 357–358 in the Student Book.

Quarters and Pennies

> ## Count on by 1s from 25¢.
>
>
>
> 25¢, 26¢, 27¢, 28¢, 29¢

Count on. Write how much.

1.

25¢, 26¢, 27¢

 27¢

2.

_____¢, _____¢, _____¢, _____¢

 _____¢

3.

_____¢, _____¢

 _____¢

4.

_____¢, _____¢, _____¢, _____¢, _____¢, _____¢

 _____¢

106 one hundred six

Use with Lesson 8-3, pages 357–358 in the Student Book.
Then go to Lesson 8-4, pages 359–360 in the Student Book.

Count On by Dimes and Nickels

Name _____

Sort like coins and order from greatest to least value.

Then count on.

10¢, 20¢, 30¢, 35¢, 40¢

Count on. Write how much.

1.

10¢, 20¢, 30¢, 35¢, 40¢, 45¢   45¢

2.

_____¢, _____¢, _____¢, _____¢, _____¢   _____¢

3.

_____¢, _____¢, _____¢, _____¢, _____¢, _____¢   _____¢

4.

_____¢, _____¢, _____¢, _____¢, _____¢, _____¢   _____¢

Use with Lesson 8-4, pages 359–360 in the Student Book.
Then go to Lesson 8-5, pages 361–362 in the Student Book.

Count Mixed Coins

Name _____

Sort like coins and order from greatest to least value.

Then count on.   25¢, 35¢, 45¢, 50¢, 51¢

Count on. Write how much.

1.

25¢, 35¢, 40¢, 41¢, 42¢, 43¢   43¢

2.

____¢, ____¢, ____¢, ____¢, ____¢, ____¢   ____¢

3.

____¢, ____¢, ____¢, ____¢, ____¢   ____¢

4.

____¢, ____¢, ____¢, ____¢, ____¢   ____¢

Copyright © by William H. Sadlier, Inc. All rights reserved.

108 one hundred eight

Use with Lesson 8-5, pages 361–362 in the Student Book.
Then go to Lesson 8-6, pages 365–366 in the Student Book.

Equal Amounts

5¢, 10¢, **15¢** | 10¢, **15¢** | 10¢, 11¢, 12¢, 13¢, 14¢, **15¢**

Write each amount.
Circle the amounts that are equal.

1.

⟨ 27¢ ⟩

 _____ ¢

 _____ ¢

2.  _____ ¢

 _____ ¢

 _____ ¢

3.  _____ ¢

 _____ ¢

 _____ ¢

4.  _____ ¢

 _____ ¢

 _____ ¢

Use with Lesson 8-6, pages 365–366 in the Student Book.
Then go to Lesson 8-7, pages 367–368 in the Student Book.

Spending Money

Is there enough money to buy a for 47¢?

$$43¢ < 47¢$$

25¢,   35¢,   40¢,   41¢,   42¢,   43¢

There is not enough money to buy the . 🙁

Write the amount you have. Draw 🙂 or 🙁
to tell if you have enough money to buy the toy.

1.

58¢   25¢, 35¢, 45¢, 55¢, 60¢   🙂

2.

46¢   ____¢, ____¢, ____¢, ____¢, ____¢

3.

33¢   ____¢, ____¢, ____¢, ____¢, ____¢

4.

57¢   ____¢, ____¢, ____¢, ____¢, ____¢

Use with Lesson 8-7, pages 367–368 in the Student Book.
Then go to Lesson 8-8, pages 369–370 in the Student Book.

One Dollar

Name _____

Skip count to show $1.

one dollar = 100 cents
$1 = 100¢

25¢,   50¢,   75¢,   100¢

Skip count. Circle to show $1.

1.

2.

3.

4.

Use with Lesson 8-8, pages 369–370 in the Student Book.
Then go to Lesson 8-9, pages 373–374 in the Student Book.

Hour

Read the time on each clock as 3 o'clock.

Write the time shown.

1.

_____ o'clock

2.

_____ o'clock

3.

_____ o'clock

4.

_____ o'clock

5.

_____ o'clock

6.

_____ o'clock

7.

_____ o'clock

8.

_____ o'clock

9.

_____ o'clock

10.

_____ o'clock

11.

_____ o'clock

12.

_____ o'clock

Use with Lesson 8-9, pages 373–374 in the Student Book.
Then go to Lesson 8-10, pages 375–376 in the Student Book.

Half Hour

There are 30 minutes in 1 half hour.

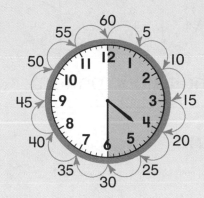

4:30

Read this time as:
4 thirty
half past 4
30 minutes after 4

Write the time in two ways.

1.

half past ___

2.

____ thirty

3.

____ minutes after ____

4.

half past ____

5.

____ thirty

6.

____ minutes after ____

7.

half past ____

Use with Lesson 8-10, pages 375–376 in the Student Book.
Then go to Lesson 8-11, pages 377–378 in the Student Book.

Time Patterns

Name _____

   |

This is an hour pattern. | This is a half-hour pattern.

Write or draw to complete each time pattern.
Circle to show the type of pattern.

1.

 o'clock   o'clock   _____ o'clock

half hour

(hour)

2. 8:00   8:30   [ ]

_____ o'clock   _____ thirty   _____ o'clock

half hour

hour

3.

_____ o'clock   _____ thirty   _____ o'clock

half hour

hour

4.  10:30   11:30   [ ]

_____ thirty   _____ thirty   half past _____

half hour

hour

Use with Lesson 8-11, pages 377–378 in the Student Book.
Then go to Lesson 8-12, pages 379–380 in the Student Book.

Elapsed Time

Name _____

9:30 to 10:30 is 1 hour.

Draw or write the time to show how long each activity takes. Circle how long.

1. | Read a book. |

Begin at 1:30.

End at 2:30.

1 half hour

(1 hour)

---

2. | Eat breakfast. |

Begin at 5:30.

End at 6:30.

1 half hour

1 hour

---

3. | Eat dinner. |

Begin at 6:30.

6:30 to _____

End at 7:00.

1 half hour

1 hour

---

4. | Do homework. |

Begin at 4:00.

_____ to _____

End at 5:00.

1 half hour

1 hour

Use with Lesson 8-12, pages 379–380 in the Student Book.
Then go to Lesson 8-13, pages 381–382 in the Student Book.

one hundred fifteen **115**

Estimate Time

Name _____

To estimate time means to tell about how long it takes to do something.

brush your teeth

about 1 minute

go to the dentist

about 1 hour

Color to show how long.

1. make a cake

about 1 minute

about 1 hour

2. take a picture

about 1 minute

about 1 hour

3. do a puzzle

about 1 minute

about 1 hour

4. do laundry

about 1 minute

about 1 hour

5. tie a shoe

about 1 minute

about 1 hour

6. open a present

about 1 minute

about 1 hour

Use with Lesson 8-13, pages 381–382 in the Student Book.
Then go to Lesson 8-14, pages 383–384 in the Student Book.

Order Events

Name _____

Many events, or activities, happen in an order.

Write morning, afternoon, or evening
to order these events.

1.

afternoon _____ _____

2.

_____ _____ _____

3.

_____ _____ _____

Use with Lesson 8-14, pages 383–384 in the Student Book.
Then go to Lesson 8-15, pages 387–388 in the Student Book.

one hundred seventeen **117**

Ordinals to 31st

Name _____

Ten toys are on the shelf.
The ordinal of the next toy put on the shelf is 11th.

11th 12th 13th 14th 15th 16th 17th 18th 19th 20th

31st 30th 29th 28th 27th 26th 25th 24th 23rd 22nd 21st

Write the ordinal number for each toy.

1. 27th

2. _____

3. _____

4. _____

5. _____

6. _____

7. _____

8. _____

9. _____

10. _____

11. _____

12. _____

Use with Lesson 8-15, pages 387–388 in the Student Book.
Then go to Lesson 8-16, pages 389–390 in the Student Book.

Calendar

Name _____

November						
Sunday	Monday	Tuesday	Wednesday	Thursday	Friday	Saturday
			1	2	3	4
5	6	7	8	9	10	11
12	13	14	15	16	17	18
19	20	21	22	23	24	25
26	27	28	29	30		

Use the calendar above to answer each question.

1. The day November 1 falls on is ____Wednesday____.

2. November has _____ days.

3. The date for the first Tuesday is _____.

4. November has _____ Mondays and _____ Thursdays.

5. One week after November 15 falls on a _____.

6. The last day of November falls on a _____.

7. The day December 1 falls on is a _____.

Use with Lesson 8-16, pages 389–390 in the Student Book.
Then go to Lessons 8-17 and 8-18, pages 391–394 in the Student Book.

one hundred nineteen **119**

Problem-Solving Strategy: Logical Reasoning

Name _____

Read Tom arrives at school at 8:30.
Jack arrives last.
Kate and Rachel arrive after Tom.
Who gets to school second?

Plan Make a list. Put the facts in the order that they happen.

Write

When	Who
8:30	Tom
next	Kate and Rachel
last	Jack

Kate and Rachel get to school second.

Check Read the problem again to be sure your facts are in the correct order.

Use logical reasoning to solve the problem.

1. Grandpa goes to sleep at 10:00.
Amy goes to bed before Grandpa.
Justin goes to bed after Grandpa.
Who goes to bed last?

When	Who
before Grandpa	
10:00	
after Grandpa	

_____ goes to bed last.

Use with Lesson 8-18, pages 393–394 in the Student Book.
Then go to Lesson 8-19, pages 395–396 in the Student Book.

Problem-Solving Applications: Mixed Strategies

Name _____

Read ❯ **Plan** ❯ **Write** ❯ **Check**

Use a strategy you have learned.

Strategy File

Logical Reasoning
Draw a Picture
Make a Table
Choose the Operation

1. Cora's shape has 6 corners.
Paula's shape has 3 sides.
Abbey's shape has 2 more
corners than Paula's.
Circle Abbey's shape.

2. Tamara is thinking of a
number greater than 40.
It is an odd number.
It has more ones than tens.
What is Tamara's number?

37   49   51   32

Tamara's number is _____.

3. Anna is eighth in line.
Carl is 3 places behind her.
The man behind Carl is last in line.
What is Carl's position in line?

Carl is _____ in line.

4. Andrea has 6 🪙.
Erika has 1 🪙.
How much money do they have altogether?

They have _____ altogether.

Length and Height: Nonstandard Units

Name _____

Length is how long something is.
Height is how tall something is.

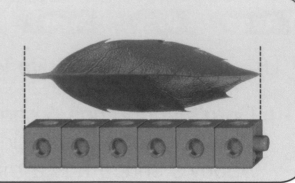

The is about 6 long.

Use  to measure the length or height of each picture.

1.

about ___7___

2.

about _____

3.

about _____

4.

about _____

5.

about _____

C Use after Lessons 9-1 and 9-2, pages 407–410 in the Student Book.
C Then go to Lesson 9-1A, pages 209–210 in this Workbook.

Perimeter

Name _____

Perimeter is the distance around a figure.

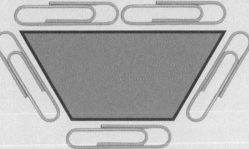

There are 5  around the figure.

The perimeter is about 5 .

Use small  to find the perimeter.

1.

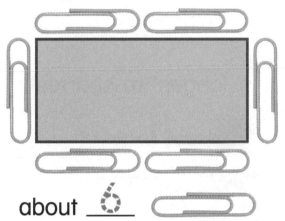

about __6__

2.

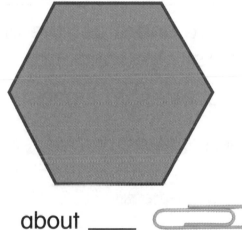

about ____

3.

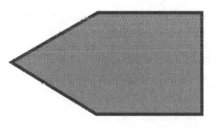

about ____

4.

about ____

5.

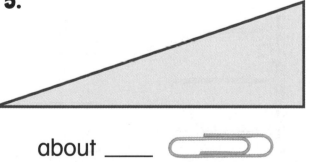

about ____

6.

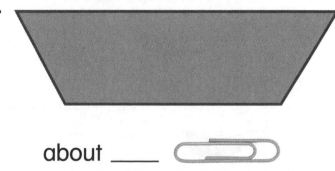

about ____

Use with Lesson 9-3, pages 411–412 in the Student Book.
Then go to Lesson 9-4, pages 413–414 in the Student Book.

Compare Lengths

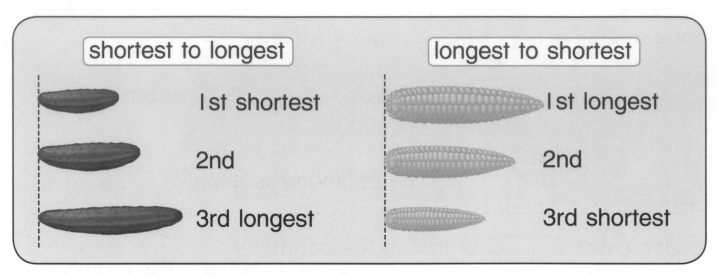

shortest to longest	longest to shortest
1st shortest	1st longest
2nd	2nd
3rd longest	3rd shortest

Compare and order the objects.
Write 1st, 2nd, and 3rd.

shortest to longest	longest to shortest

1.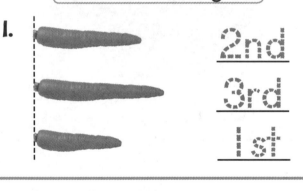

2nd

3rd

1st

4.

_____

_____

_____

2.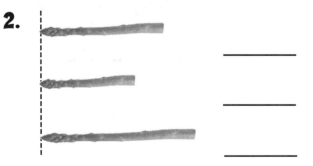

_____

_____

_____

5.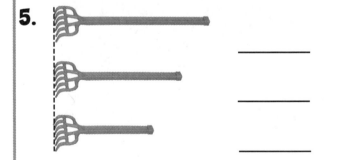

_____

_____

_____

3.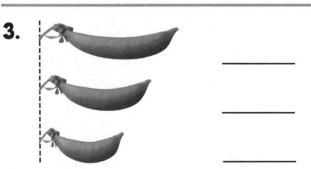

_____

_____

_____

6.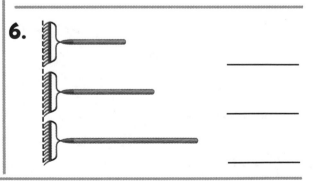

_____

_____

_____

one hundred twenty-four

Use with Lesson 9-4, pages 413–414 in the Student Book.
Then go to Lessons 9-4A and 9-4B, pages 211–214 in this Workbook.

Copyright © by William H. Sadlier, Inc. All rights reserved.

Inches

Name _____

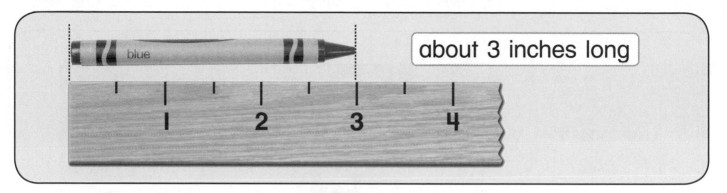

about 3 inches long

Measure the length or height of each picture in inches.

1.

about __4__ inches

2.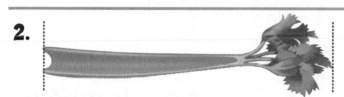

about ____ inches

3.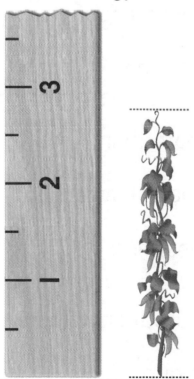

about ____ inches

4.

about ____ inches

5.

about ____ inch

6.

about ____ inches

Use with Lesson 9-5, pages 415–416 in the Student Book.
Then go to Lesson 9-6, pages 417–418 in the Student Book.

one hundred twenty-five **125**

Feet

Name _____

less than 1 foot | about 1 foot | more than 1 foot

Think about these real objects.
Estimate the length of each real object.
Circle the most reasonable estimate.

1.

(more than 1 foot)

about 1 foot

less than 1 foot

2.

more than 1 foot

about 1 foot

less than 1 foot

3.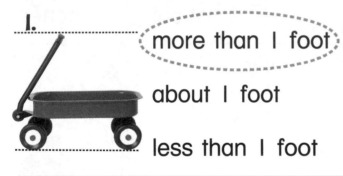

more than 1 foot

about 1 foot

less than 1 foot

4.

more than 1 foot

about 1 foot

less than 1 foot

5.

more than 1 foot

about 1 foot

less than 1 foot

6.

more than 1 foot

about 1 foot

less than 1 foot

Use with Lesson 9-6, pages 417–418 in the Student Book.
Then go to Lessons 9-7 and 9-8, pages 419–424 in the Student Book.

Capacity: Nonstandard Units

Name _____

Use a to estimate about how much each container holds.

about 1   about 10   about 60

Estimate about how many  each real container holds.

1.

2    (10)

2.

5   50

3.

6   20

4.

4   40

5.

10   25

6.

2   10

Use with Lesson 9-8, pages 423–424 in the Student Book.
Then go to Lessons 9-9 and 9-10, pages 425–428 in the Student Book.

one hundred twenty-seven **127**

Cups, Pints, and Quarts

Name _____

2 cups = 1 pint   2 pints = 1 quart

Circle which holds more.

1. or

2.  or

3.  or

4.  or

Write how many.

5. 2 = ____

6. 2  = ____

7. 8 = ____

8. 6 = ____

Use after Lessons 9-9 and 9-10, pages 425–428 in the Student Book.
Then go to Lesson 9-11, pages 429–430 in the Student Book.

Weight: Nonstandard Units

Name _____

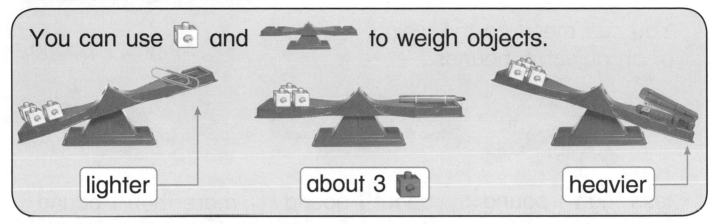

You can use 📷 and ⚖️ to weigh objects.

lighter   about 3 📷   heavier

Compare the weight of these objects.
Circle the object that is heavier. ✗ the object that is lighter.

1.

2.

3.

4.

5.

6.

7.

8.

Use with Lesson 9-11, pages 429–430 in the Student Book.
Then go to Lesson 9-12, pages 431–432 in the Student Book.

one hundred twenty-nine **129**

Pounds

Name _____

You can measure the weight of an object in pounds. 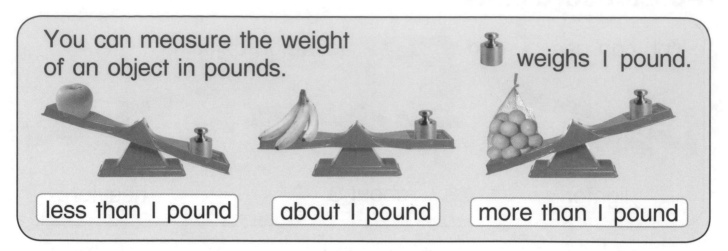 weighs 1 pound.

| less than 1 pound | about 1 pound | more than 1 pound |

Think about these real objects.
Circle about how much each object weighs.

1.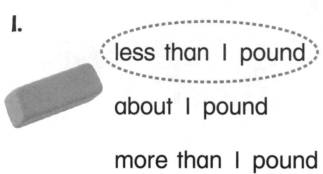
(less than 1 pound)
about 1 pound
more than 1 pound

2.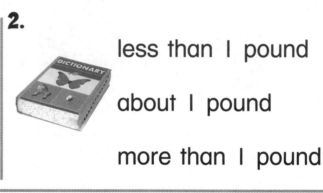
less than 1 pound
about 1 pound
more than 1 pound

3.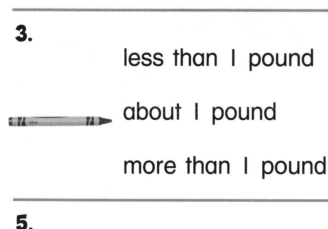
less than 1 pound
about 1 pound
more than 1 pound

4.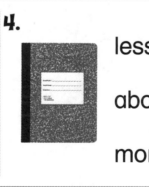
less than 1 pound
about 1 pound
more than 1 pound

5.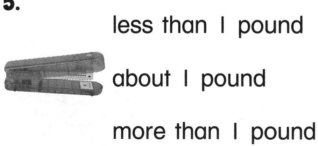
less than 1 pound
about 1 pound
more than 1 pound

6.
less than 1 pound
about 1 pound
more than 1 pound

Use with Lesson 9-12, pages 431–432 in the Student Book.
Then go to Lesson 9-13, pages 435–436 in the Student Book.

Centimeters

Name _____

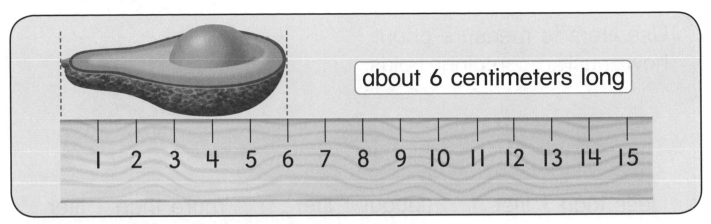

about 6 centimeters long

Use a centimeter ruler to measure the length of each picture.

1.

about __9__ centimeters

2.

about ____ centimeters

3.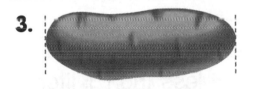

about ____ centimeters

Measure the height in centimeters.

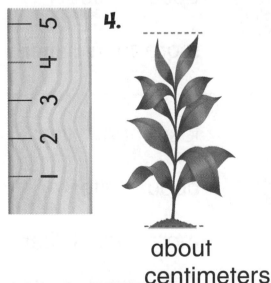

4.

about ____ centimeters

5.

about ____ centimeters

6.

about ____ centimeters

Use with Lesson 9-13, pages 435–436 in the Student Book.
Then go to Lesson 9-14, pages 437–438 in the Student Book.

one hundred thirty-one **131**

Liters

Name _____

Use liters to measure about how much a container holds.

less than I liter

about I liter

more than I liter

Circle about how much each real container holds.

1.

less than I liter

about I liter

(more than I liter)

2.

less than I liter

about I liter

more than I liter

3.

less than I liter

about I liter

more than I liter

4.

less than I liter

about I liter

more than I liter

5.

less than I liter

about I liter

more than I liter

6.

less than I liter

about I liter

more than I liter

Use with Lesson 9-14, pages 437–438 in the Student Book.
Then go to Lesson 9-15, pages 439–440 in the Student Book.

Kilograms

Name _____

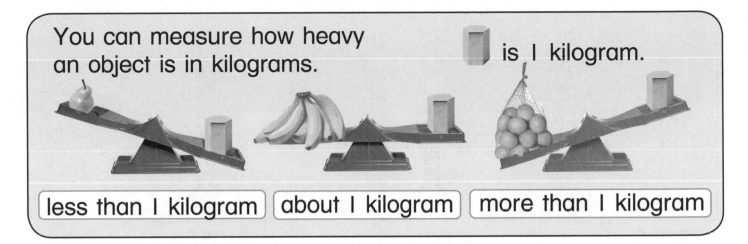

You can measure how heavy an object is in kilograms.

is I kilogram.

| less than I kilogram | about I kilogram | more than I kilogram |

Circle about how heavy.

1.

(less than I kilogram)

about I kilogram

more than I kilogram

2.

less than I kilogram

about I kilogram

more than I kilogram

3.

less than I kilogram

about I kilogram

more than I kilogram

4.

less than I kilogram

about I kilogram

more than I kilogram

5.

less than I kilogram

about I kilogram

more than I kilogram

6.

less than I kilogram

about I kilogram

more than I kilogram

Use with Lesson 9-15, pages 439–440 in the Student Book.
Then go to Lessons 9-16 and 9-17, pages 441–444 in the Student Book.

one hundred thirty-three **133**

Temperature; Seasons

Name _____

20°F   cold   50°F   cool   80°F   hot

Read each thermometer. Write the temperature.

1.  60 °F

2.  _____ °F

3.  _____ °F

4. Draw lines to match the season with the picture.

winter

spring

summer

fall

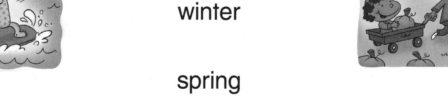

Use after Lessons 9-16 and 9-17, pages 441–444 in the Student Book.
Then go to Lesson 9-18, pages 445–446 in the Student Book.

Choose a Measuring Tool

Name _____

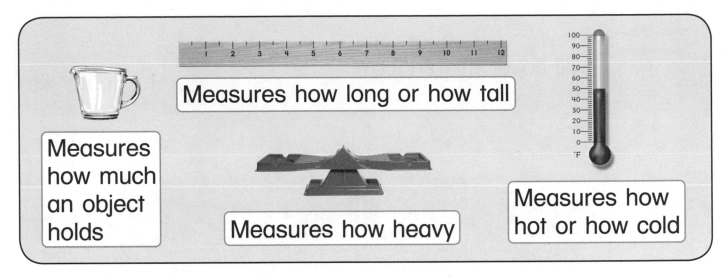

Measures how long or how tall

Measures how much an object holds

Measures how heavy

Measures how hot or how cold

Circle the tool you would use to measure.

1. How much does it hold?

2. How hot is it?

3. How much does it weigh?

4. How long is it?

5. How much does it hold?

6. How much does it weigh?

Use with Lesson 9-18, pages 445–446 in the Student Book.
Then go to Lesson 9-19, pages 447–448 in the Student Book.

Problem-Solving Strategy: Make a Model

Name _____

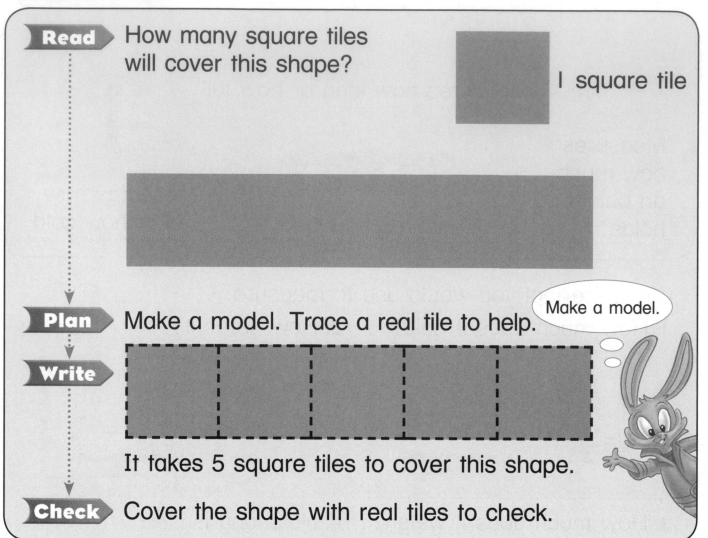

Read How many square tiles will cover this shape?

I square tile

Plan Make a model. Trace a real tile to help.

Make a model.

Write

It takes 5 square tiles to cover this shape.

Check Cover the shape with real tiles to check.

Use ▢ to solve the question.

I. How many square tiles will cover the shape?

_____ ▢ will cover this shape.

Use with Lesson 9-19, pages 447–448 in the Student Book.
Then go to Lesson 9-20, pages 449–450 in the Student Book.

Problem-Solving Applications: Mixed Strategies

Name _____

Read > **Plan** > **Write** > **Check**

Use a strategy you have learned.

Strategy File

Find/Use a Pattern
Logical Reasoning
Draw a Picture
Make a Table

1. Simon saves a (nickel) every day for 10 days. How much does he save in all?

Simon saves _____ in all.

2. Tad writes five 2-digit numbers.
They are between 44 and 66.
They all have either 5 or 0 in the ones place.
What numbers does Tad write?

_____, _____, _____, _____, _____

3. Find a pattern.
Write the same pattern using letters and numbers.

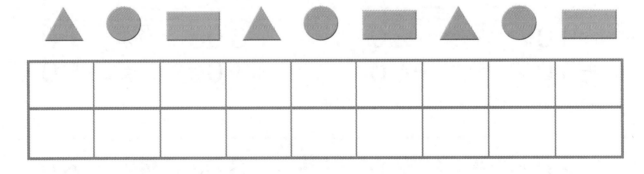

4. José has 7 dinner plates.
He breaks 3 plates at dinner.
How many plates does José have left?

José has _____ plates left.

Add Tens and Dimes

Name ______________________

1 ten	10		1 dime	10¢	
+3 tens	+30		+3 dimes	+30¢	
4 tens	40		4 dimes	40¢	
4 tens = 40			4 dimes = 40¢		

Add. Use or to help.

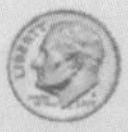

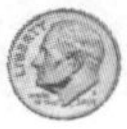

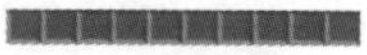

1.

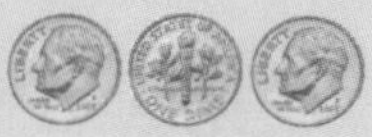

6 dimes + 2 dimes = 8 dimes

60¢ + 20¢ = 80¢

2.

4 tens + 3 tens = ___ tens

☐ + ☐ = ___

3.

5 tens + 2 tens = ___ tens

☐ + ☐ = ___

4.

1 dime + 4 dimes = ___ dimes

☐ + ☐ = ___

5. 40 + 50 = 90

6. 20 + 60 = ___

7. 80¢ + 10¢ = ___

8. 10 + 50 = ___

9. 20¢ + 40¢ = ___

10. 70 + 20 = ___

11. 30¢ + 10¢ = ___

12. 60 + 30 = ___

13. 30 + 40 = ___

14. 10 + 70 = ___

Use with Lesson 10-1, pages 465–466 in the Student Book.
Then go to Lesson 10-2, pages 467–468 in the Student Book.

Add Ones and Tens Using Models

Name _____

38 + 21 = ?

Model the addends.	Add the ones.	Then add the tens.

tens	ones

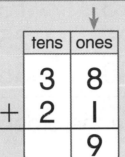

	tens	ones
	3	8
+	2	1
		9

	tens	ones
	3	8
+	2	1
	5	9

38 + 21 = 59

Add. Use ▬▬▬▬ and ▪.

1.

	tens	ones
	4	2
+	2	4
	6	6

tens	ones

2.

	tens	ones
	1	2
+	3	5

tens	ones

3.

	tens	ones
	2	2
+	2	2

tens	ones

4.

	tens	ones
	4	1
+	1	5

tens	ones

5.

	tens	ones
	3	7
+	1	2

tens	ones

6.

	tens	ones
	1	4
+	4	3

tens	ones

C Use with Lesson 10-2, pages 467–468 in the Student Book.
C Then go to Lesson 10-2A, pages 215–216 in this Workbook.

Add Ones and Tens Without Models

Name _____

Add the ones, then add the tens.

Change the order of the addends to check the sum.

$$
\begin{array}{r} 13 \\ +25 \\ \hline 38 \end{array}
\qquad
\begin{array}{r} 13 \\ +25 \\ \hline 38 \end{array}
\times
\begin{array}{r} 25 \\ +13 \\ \hline 38 \end{array}
$$

Find the sum. Change the order to check.

1.
$$
\begin{array}{r} 21 \\ +56 \\ \hline 77 \end{array}
\qquad
\begin{array}{r} 56 \\ +21 \\ \hline 77 \end{array}
$$
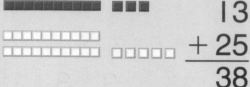

2.
$$
\begin{array}{r} 73 \\ +24 \\ \hline \end{array}
\qquad + \square
$$

3.
$$
\begin{array}{r} 50 \\ +39 \\ \hline \end{array}
\qquad + \square
$$

4.
$$
\begin{array}{r} 22 \\ +43 \\ \hline \end{array}
\qquad + \square
$$

5.
$$
\begin{array}{r} 45 \\ +12 \\ \hline \end{array}
\qquad + \square
$$

6.
$$
\begin{array}{r} 34 \\ +62 \\ \hline \end{array}
\qquad + \square
$$

7.
$$
\begin{array}{r} 23 \\ +13 \\ \hline \end{array}
\qquad + \square
$$

8.
$$
\begin{array}{r} 47 \\ +31 \\ \hline \end{array}
\qquad + \square
$$

9.
$$
\begin{array}{r} 65 \\ +24 \\ \hline \end{array}
\qquad + \square
$$

10.
$$
\begin{array}{r} 81 \\ +15 \\ \hline \end{array}
\qquad + \square
$$

11.
$$
\begin{array}{r} 43 \\ +42 \\ \hline \end{array}
\qquad + \square
$$

12.
$$
\begin{array}{r} 66 \\ +30 \\ \hline \end{array}
\qquad + \square
$$

13.
$$
\begin{array}{r} 57 \\ +40 \\ \hline \end{array}
\qquad + \square
$$

14.
$$
\begin{array}{r} 64 \\ +15 \\ \hline \end{array}
\qquad + \square
$$

15.
$$
\begin{array}{r} 28 \\ +70 \\ \hline \end{array}
\qquad + \square
$$

140 one hundred forty

C Use with Lesson 10-3, pages 469–470 in the Student Book.
C Then go to Lesson 10-4, pages 471–472 in the Student Book.

Add Money

$11¢ + 21¢ = ?$

Model each amount.

dimes	pennies

Add the pennies.

dimes	pennies
1	1
+ 2	1
	2

Add the dimes.

dimes	pennies
1	1
+ 2	1
3	2

$11¢ + 21¢ = 32¢$

Use 🪙 and 🪙 to add.

1.

dimes	pennies
2	1
+ 4	7
6	8

```
  21¢
+ 47¢
  68¢
```

2.

dimes	pennies
3	4
+ 2	5

```
  34¢
+ 25¢
```

3.
```
  56¢
+ 32¢
```

4.
```
  76¢
+ 13¢
```

5.
```
  43¢
+ 34¢
```

6.
```
  42¢
+ 43¢
```

7.
```
  39¢
+ 30¢
```

8.
```
  15¢
+ 44¢
```

9.
```
  24¢
+ 52¢
```

10.
```
  82¢
+ 17¢
```

11.
```
  33¢
+ 50¢
```

12.
```
  62¢
+ 12¢
```

C Use with Lesson 10-4, pages 471–472 in the Student Book.
C Then go to Lesson 10-4A, pages 217–218 in this Workbook.

Add Ones or Tens

Name _____

$$52 + 2 = ?$$

Start at 52.
Count on 2 ones.

$$+1 \quad +1$$

52, 53, 54

$$52 + 2 = 54$$

$$52 + 20 = ?$$

Start at 52.
Count on 2 tens.

$$+10 \quad +10$$

52, 62, 72

$$52 + 20 = 72$$

Add. Count on by ones or by tens.

1.
$$\begin{array}{r} 38 \\ +\ 1 \\ \hline 39 \end{array} \qquad \begin{array}{r} 38 \\ +10 \\ \hline 48 \end{array}$$

2.
$$\begin{array}{r} 11 \\ +\ 2 \\ \hline \end{array} \qquad \begin{array}{r} 11 \\ +20 \\ \hline \end{array}$$

3.
$$\begin{array}{r} 24 \\ +\ 1 \\ \hline \end{array} \qquad \begin{array}{r} 24 \\ +10 \\ \hline \end{array}$$

4.
$$\begin{array}{r} 62 \\ +\ 3 \\ \hline \end{array} \qquad \begin{array}{r} 62 \\ +30 \\ \hline \end{array}$$

5.
$$\begin{array}{r} 45 \\ +\ 4 \\ \hline \end{array} \qquad \begin{array}{r} 45 \\ +40 \\ \hline \end{array}$$

6.
$$\begin{array}{r} 57 \\ +\ 2 \\ \hline \end{array} \qquad \begin{array}{r} 57 \\ +20 \\ \hline \end{array}$$

7.
$$63 + 20 = \underline{\quad\quad}$$
$$63 + 2 = \underline{\quad\quad}$$

8.
$$31 + 3 = \underline{\quad\quad}$$
$$31 + 30 = \underline{\quad\quad}$$

9.
$$37 + 2 = \underline{\quad\quad}$$
$$37 + 20 = \underline{\quad\quad}$$

10.
$$16 + 3 = \underline{\quad\quad}$$
$$16 + 30 = \underline{\quad\quad}$$

11.
$$24¢ + 30¢ = \underline{\quad\quad}$$
$$24¢ + 3¢ = \underline{\quad\quad}$$

12.
$$51¢ + 1¢ = \underline{\quad\quad}$$
$$51¢ + 10¢ = \underline{\quad\quad}$$

Use with Lesson 10-5, pages 473–474 in the Student Book.
Then go to Lessons 10-5A and 10-5B, pages 219–222 in this Workbook.

Nearest Ten

Name _____

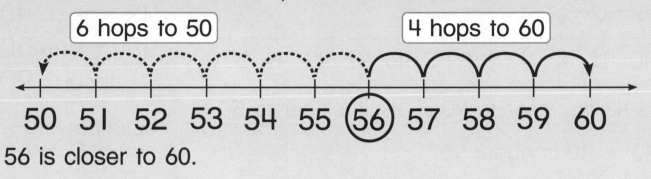

Is 56 closer to 50 or 60?

To find the closer number, find the nearest ten.

6 hops to 50   4 hops to 60

50 51 52 53 54 55 (56) 57 58 59 60

56 is closer to 60.

Draw hops to find the nearest ten.

1. Is 73 closer to 70 or 80?

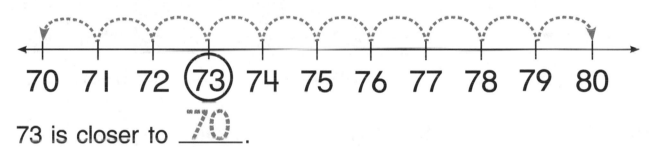

70 71 72 (73) 74 75 76 77 78 79 80

73 is closer to __70__.

2. Is 68 closer to 60 or 70?

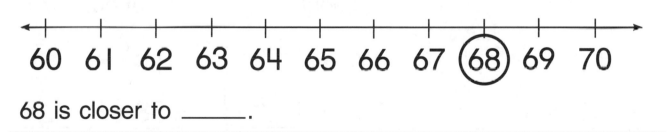

60 61 62 63 64 65 66 67 (68) 69 70

68 is closer to _____.

3. Is 24 closer to 20 or 30?

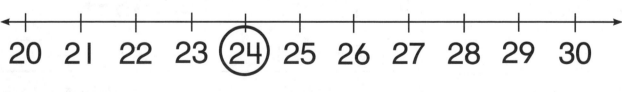

20 21 22 23 (24) 25 26 27 28 29 30

24 is closer to _____.

Use with Lesson 10-6, pages 475–476 in the Student Book.
Then go to Lesson 10-7, pages 477–478 in the Student Book.

Estimate Sums

Estimate the sum of 43 + 49.

Find the nearest ten for each addend.

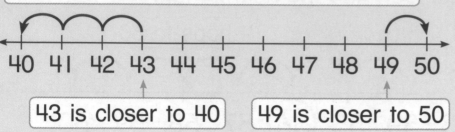

43 is closer to 40   49 is closer to 50

43 + 49 is about 90.

Then add the nearest tens.

$$43 \longrightarrow 40$$
$$+49 \longrightarrow +50$$
$$\text{about} \quad 90$$

estimate

Estimate the sum.

1. $22 \rightarrow \boxed{20}$
$+41 \rightarrow +\boxed{40}$
about 60

2. $39 \rightarrow \boxed{}$
$+32 \rightarrow +\boxed{}$
about

3. $76 \rightarrow \boxed{}$
$+12 \rightarrow +\boxed{}$
about

4. $57 \rightarrow \boxed{}$
$+17 \rightarrow +\boxed{}$
about

5. $28 \rightarrow \boxed{}$
$+62 \rightarrow +\boxed{}$
about

6. $54 \rightarrow \boxed{}$
$+23 \rightarrow +\boxed{}$
about

7. $11 \rightarrow \boxed{}$
$+81 \rightarrow +\boxed{}$
about

8. $16 \rightarrow \boxed{}$
$+71 \rightarrow +\boxed{}$
about

9. $14 \rightarrow \boxed{}$
$+58 \rightarrow +\boxed{}$
about

10. $42 \rightarrow \boxed{}$
$+53 \rightarrow +\boxed{}$
about

11. $19 \rightarrow \boxed{}$
$+36 \rightarrow +\boxed{}$
about

12. $46 \rightarrow \boxed{}$
$+37 \rightarrow +\boxed{}$
about

Use with Lesson 10-7, pages 477–478 in the Student Book.
Then go to Lessons 10-8 and 10-9, pages 479–484 in the Student Book.

Regroup Ones as Tens Using Models

Regroup 1 ten 17 ones.

Model 1 ten 17 ones.	Regroup 10 ones as 1 ten.

 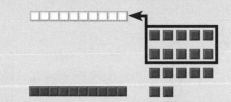

1 ten 17 ones = 2 tens 7 ones

Use �■ and ■.
Regroup 10 ones as 1 ten.

1.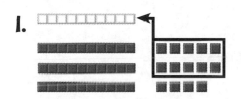

3 tens 14 ones = __4__ tens __4__ ones

2.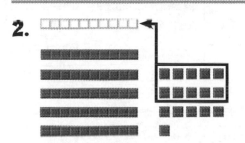

5 tens 16 ones = ____ tens ____ ones

3.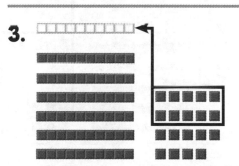

6 tens 19 ones = ____ tens ____ ones

4.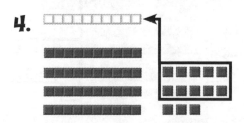

4 tens 13 ones = ____ tens ____ ones

☞ Use with Lesson 10-9, pages 483–484 in the Student Book.
☞ Then go to Lesson 10-10, pages 485–486 in the Student Book.

Regroup Ones as Tens Using a Chart

Name _____

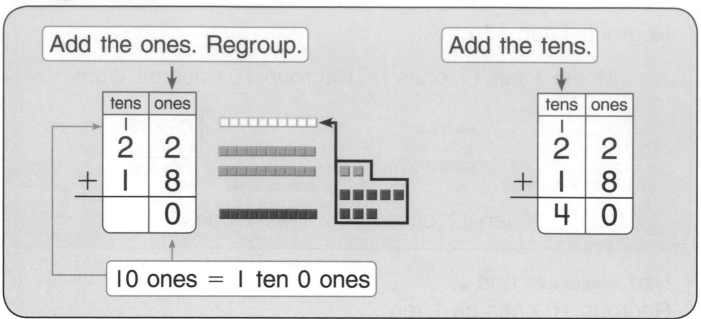

Add the ones. Regroup.

tens	ones
1	
2	2
+ 1	8
	0

10 ones = 1 ten 0 ones

Add the tens.

tens	ones
1	
2	2
+ 1	8
4	0

Find the sum.

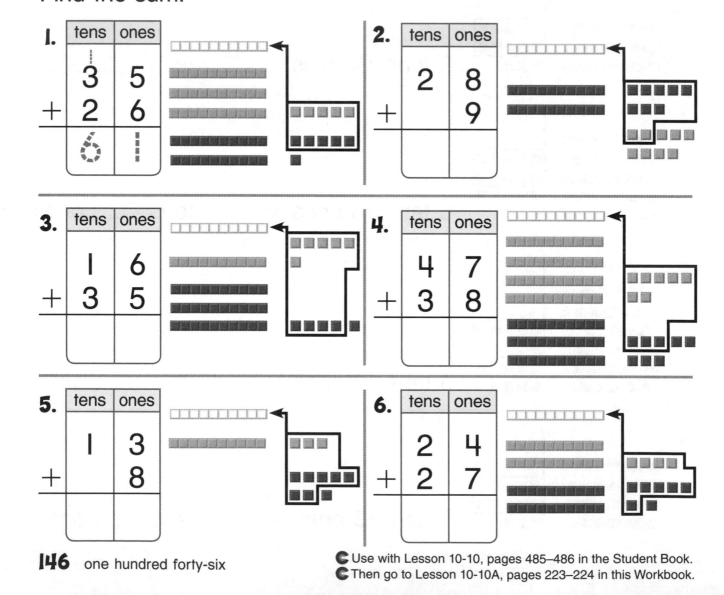

1.

tens	ones
3	5
+ 2	6
6	1

2.

tens	ones
2	8
+	9

3.

tens	ones
1	6
+ 3	5

4.

tens	ones
4	7
+ 3	8

5.

tens	ones
1	3
+	8

6.

tens	ones
2	4
+ 2	7

146 one hundred forty-six

Use with Lesson 10-10, pages 485–486 in the Student Book.
Then go to Lesson 10-10A, pages 223–224 in this Workbook.

Regroup Money

Name _____

$23¢ + 19¢ = ?$

Model the amounts.
Regroup. 10 pennies = 1 dime

Add the pennies.
Regroup 10 pennies
as 1 dime.
Add the dimes.

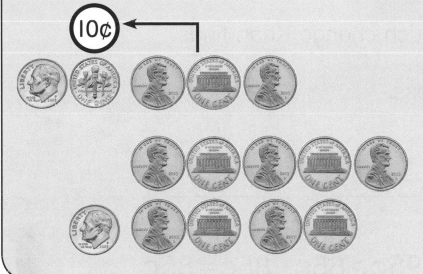

dimes	pennies
¹2	3
+ 1	9
4	2

$$23¢$$
$$+19¢$$
$$\overline{42¢}$$

Use and to find the sum.

1.

dimes	pennies
¹6	3
+ 1	7
8	0

2.

dimes	pennies
3	6
+ 3	4

3.

dimes	pennies
6	4
+ 2	6

4.
$$26¢$$
$$+17¢$$

5.
$$39¢$$
$$+ \ 8¢$$

6.
$$51¢$$
$$+19¢$$

7.
$$68¢$$
$$+18¢$$

8.
$$55¢$$
$$+ \ 6¢$$

9.
$$22¢$$
$$+68¢$$

10.
$$37¢$$
$$+54¢$$

11.
$$14¢$$
$$+79¢$$

Use with Lesson 10-11, pages 487–488 in the Student Book.
Then go to Lesson 10-12, pages 489–490 in the Student Book.

one hundred forty-seven **147**

Problem-Solving Strategy: Guess and Test

Read ▸ Khan needs 85¢ to buy a mango. | 45¢ | 65¢ | 55¢ |
He finds some change in his pocket.
Now he needs 30¢ to buy a mango.
How much change does Khan find in his pocket?

Plan ▸ Guess how much change Khan finds.

Write ▸ Test each guess.

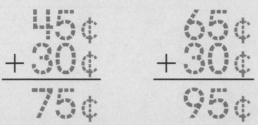

$$45¢ + 30¢ = 75¢ \qquad 65¢ + 30¢ = 95¢ \qquad 55¢ + 30¢ = 85¢$$

75¢ < 85¢   95¢ > 85¢   85¢ = 85¢
not enough   too much   ✔

Khan finds 55¢.

Check ▸ Use real coins to check.

Guess and test to find the answer.

| 1 | 11 | 21 |

1. Sarah has 5 🍒.
Joanna has some, too.
Together they have 26 🍒.
How many 🍒 does
Joanna have?

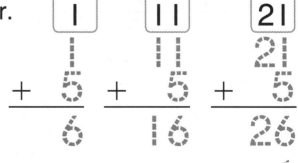

$$+ \; 5 \qquad + \; 5 \qquad + \; 5$$
$$6 \qquad 16 \qquad 26$$

Joanna has _____ 🍒.

2. Diaz has 2 .
One 🍐 costs 68¢.
How much more money
does Diaz need to buy one 🍐?

| 48¢ | 18¢ | 58¢ |

Diaz needs _____.

Use with Lesson 10-12, pages 489–490 in the Student Book.
Then go to Lesson 10-13, pages 491–492 in the Student Book.

Problem-Solving Applications: Mixed Strategies

Name _____

Read ▸ **Plan** ▸ **Write** ▸ **Check**

Use a strategy you have learned.

Strategy File
Make a Table
Choose the Operation
Logical Reasoning

1. Sybil plants 10 flowers in a minute.
How many flowers does she
plant in 7 minutes?

Sybil plants ____ flowers in 7 minutes.

2. Hana has 3 dimes.
Her mom gives Hana
1 penny and 2 nickels.
How much money does Hana have then?

Hana has ____.

3. At the pool, 12 children use .
6 children use .
8 children use .
How many more children use than ?

____ more children use than .

4. The sum of two numbers is 16.
The difference between the
two numbers is 2.
What are the two numbers?

The numbers are ____ and ____.

Subtract Tens and Dimes

Name _____

To subtract 50 – 30, think 5 tens – 3 tens.	To subtract 50¢ – 30¢, think 5 dimes – 3 dimes.

5 tens   50
−3 tens   −30
2 tens   20

2 tens = 20

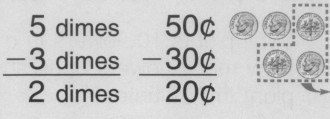

5 dimes   50¢
−3 dimes   −30¢
2 dimes   20¢

2 dimes = 20¢

Subtract. Use or ▬▬▬▬ to help.

1.
9 dimes   90¢
−7 dimes   −70¢
2 dimes   20¢

2.
6 tens
−2 tens
tens

3.
4 tens
−3 tens
ten

4.
2 dimes
−1 dime
dime

5.
70
−40
30

6.
80¢
−50¢

7.
90
−80

8.
50¢
−40¢

9.
30
−20

10.
80¢
−60¢

11.
70
−50

12.
90¢
−50¢

13. 60 − 40 = _____

14. 70¢ − 30¢ = _____

Use with Lesson 11-1, pages 503–504 in the Student Book.
Then go to Lesson 11-1A, pages 225–226 in this Workbook.

Subtract Ones and Tens Using Models

Name _____

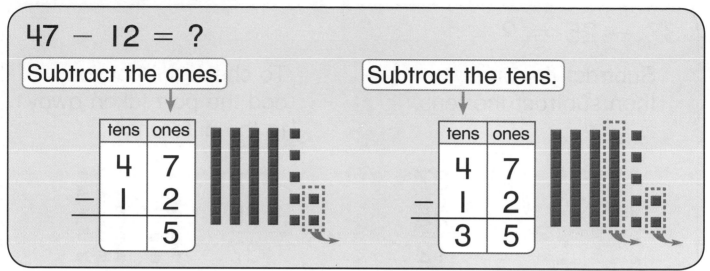

47 − 12 = ?

Subtract the ones.

tens	ones
4	7
− 1	2
	5

Subtract the tens.

tens	ones
4	7
− 1	2
3	5

Circle the ▬▬▬ and ■ you subtract.
Write the difference.

1.

tens	ones
3	4
− 2	3
┊	┊

2.

tens	ones
4	8
− 2	2

3.

tens	ones
5	6
− 3	5

4.

tens	ones
2	8
− 1	3

5.

tens	ones
5	9
− 2	5

6.

tens	ones
3	5
− 1	4

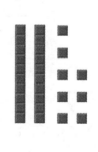

Use with Lesson 11-2, pages 505–506 in the Student Book.
Then go to Lesson 11-3, pages 507–508 in the Student Book.

Subtract Ones and Tens Without Models

Name _____

37 − 25 = ?

Subtract the ones, then subtract the tens.	To check subtraction, add the part taken away to the difference.

```
  37
− 25
  12
```

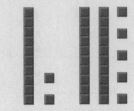

```
  12
+ 25
  37
```

Subtract. Check by adding.

1.
```
  54        41
− 13      + 13
  41        54
```

2.
```
  79
− 23      + [ ]
          [ ]
```

3.
```
  97
− 67      + [ ]
          [ ]
```

4.
```
  67
− 13      + [ ]
          [ ]
```

5.
```
  86
− 52      + [ ]
          [ ]
```

6.
```
  77
− 64      + [ ]
          [ ]
```

7.
```
  57
− 30      + [ ]
          [ ]
```

8.
```
  32
− 11      + [ ]
          [ ]
```

9.
```
  45
− 24      + [ ]
          [ ]
```

10.
```
  94
− 51      + [ ]
          [ ]
```

11.
```
  88
− 46      + [ ]
          [ ]
```

12.
```
  55
− 20      + [ ]
          [ ]
```

Use with Lesson 11-3, pages 507–508 in the Student Book.
Then go to Lesson 11-4, pages 509–510 in the Student Book.

Subtract Money

$21¢ - 11¢ = ?$

| Model the subtraction. | | Subtract pennies. | Subtract dimes. |

dimes	pennies

	dimes	pennies
	2	1
−	1	1
		0

	dimes	pennies
	2	1
−	1	1
	1	0

$21¢ - 11¢ = 10¢$

Use 🪙 and 🪙 to subtract.

1.

dimes	pennies
4	5
− 2	1
2	4

```
  45¢
 −21¢
  24¢
```

2.

dimes	pennies
3	8
− 1	6

```
  38¢
 −16¢
```

3.
```
 46¢
−13¢
```

4.
```
 87¢
−70¢
```

5.
```
 68¢
−25¢
```

6.
```
 95¢
−55¢
```

7.
```
 58¢
−31¢
```

8.
```
 66¢
−10¢
```

9.
```
 57¢
−23¢
```

10.
```
 98¢
−32¢
```

11.
```
 25¢
−14¢
```

12.
```
 76¢
−64¢
```

13.
```
 97¢
−25¢
```

14.
```
 38¢
−24¢
```

15.
```
 48¢
−33¢
```

16.
```
 95¢
−70¢
```

17.
```
 67¢
−54¢
```

Use with Lesson 11-4, pages 509–510 in the Student Book.
Then go to Lesson 11-4A, pages 229–230 in this Workbook.

Subtract Ones or Tens

Name _____

$55 - 3 = ?$

Start at 55, count back by 1s.
$-1 \quad -1 \quad -1$
55, 54, 53, 52

$55 - 3 = 52$

$55 - 30 = ?$

Start at 55, count back by 10s.
$-10 \quad -10 \quad -10$
55, 45, 35, 25

$55 - 30 = 25$

Subtract mentally. Write the difference.

1.
```
  56      56
-  4    -40
  52      16
```

2.
```
  68      68
-  3    -30
```

3.
```
  49      49
-  2    -20
```

4.
```
  96      96
-30     - 3
```

5.
```
  88      88
-10     - 1
```

6.
```
  73      73
-  2    -20
```

7.
```
  60      60
-  1    -10
```

8.
```
  25      25
-20     - 2
```

9.
```
  65      65
-  4    -40
```

10.
```
  83      83
-30     - 3
```

11.
```
  44      44
-  2    -20
```

12.
```
  37      37
-  1    -10
```

13.
$76 - 2 = $ _____
$76 - 20 = $ _____

14.
$55 - 40 = $ _____
$55 - 4 = $ _____

Use with Lesson 11-5, pages 511–512 in the Student Book.
Then go to Lessons 11-6 and 11-7, pages 513–518 in the Student Book.

Estimate Differences

Name _____

Estimate the difference of 39 − 31.

| Find the nearest ten for each. | | Then subtract. |

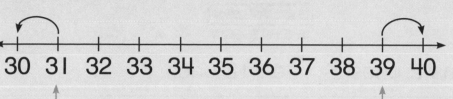

$$39 \rightarrow 40$$
$$-31 \rightarrow -30$$
$$\text{about } 10$$

31 is closer to 30   39 is closer to 40   estimate

39 − 31 is about 10.

Estimate the difference.

1.
$$68 \rightarrow 70$$
$$-24 \rightarrow -20$$
about 50

2.
$$91 \rightarrow \boxed{}$$
$$-19 \rightarrow -\boxed{}$$
about

3.
$$56 \rightarrow \boxed{}$$
$$-48 \rightarrow -\boxed{}$$
about

4.
$$33 \rightarrow \boxed{}$$
$$-12 \rightarrow -\boxed{}$$
about

5.
$$76 \rightarrow \boxed{}$$
$$-61 \rightarrow -\boxed{}$$
about

6.
$$92 \rightarrow \boxed{}$$
$$-28 \rightarrow -\boxed{}$$
about

7.
$$41 \rightarrow \boxed{}$$
$$-38 \rightarrow -\boxed{}$$
about

8.
$$87 \rightarrow \boxed{}$$
$$-41 \rightarrow -\boxed{}$$
about

9.
$$49 \rightarrow \boxed{}$$
$$-23 \rightarrow -\boxed{}$$
about

10.
$$28 \rightarrow \boxed{}$$
$$-21 \rightarrow -\boxed{}$$
about

11.
$$62 \rightarrow \boxed{}$$
$$-47 \rightarrow -\boxed{}$$
about

12.
$$83 \rightarrow \boxed{}$$
$$-39 \rightarrow -\boxed{}$$
about

Use with Lesson 11-7, pages 517–518 in the Student Book.
Then go to Lesson 11-8, pages 519–520 in the Student Book.

Regroup Tens as Ones Using Models

Name _____

| Model 2 tens 2 ones. | Regroup 1 ten as 10 ones. |

2 tens 2 ones = 1 ten 12 ones

Use ▬▬▬ and ■ .
Regroup 1 ten as 10 ones.

1.
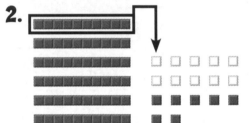

3 tens 5 ones = __2__ tens __15__ ones

2.
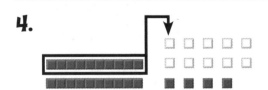

6 tens 7 ones = ____ tens ____ ones

3.
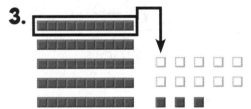

5 tens 3 ones = ____ tens ____ ones

4.
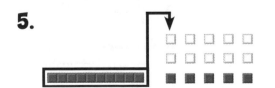

2 tens 4 ones = ____ ten ____ ones

5.

1 ten 5 ones = ____ tens ____ ones

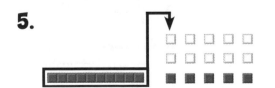

Use with Lesson 11-8, pages 519–520 in the Student Book.
Then go to Lesson 11-9, pages 521–522 in the Student Book.

Regroup Tens as Ones Using a Chart

Name _____

There are not enough ones to subtract.	Regroup 1 ten as 10 ones. Subtract. Begin with the ones.

tens	ones
3	4
− 1	5

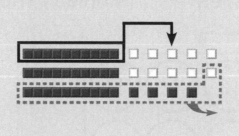

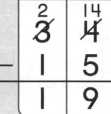

tens	ones
2̸3	¹⁴4̸
− 1	5
1	9

3 tens 4 ones = 2 tens 14 ones

Regroup 1 ten as 10 ones. Find the difference.
Circle the part you take away.

1.

tens	ones
⁵6̸	¹³3̸
− 2	6
3	7

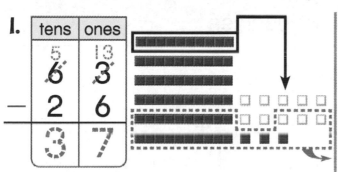

2.

tens	ones
3	5
−	8

3.

tens	ones
4	1
− 2	5

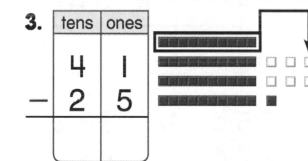

4.

tens	ones
5	8
− 3	9

5.

tens	ones
7	6
− 2	8

6.

tens	ones
6	4
− 3	8

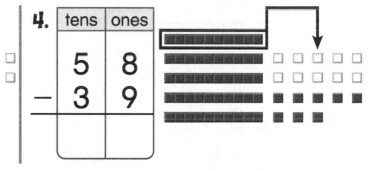

Use with Lesson 11-9, pages 521–522 in the Student Book.
Then go to Lesson 11-9A, pages 231–232 in this Workbook.

Regroup Dimes as Pennies

Name _____

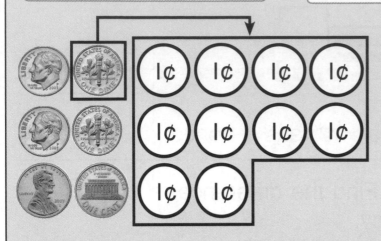

$42¢ - 24¢ = ?$

Model 42¢. Regroup 1 dime as 10 pennies.

Use the pennies from your regrouped dime to subtract the pennies. Then subtract the dimes.

dimes	pennies
3	12
4̸	2̸
− 2	4
1	8

$\begin{array}{r} \overset{3\ 12}{4\!\!\!/2}¢ \\ -24¢ \\ \hline 18¢ \end{array}$

$42¢ - 24¢ = 18¢$

4 dimes 2 pennies = 3 dimes 12 pennies

Use 🪙 and 🪙 to find the difference.

1.

dimes	pennies
4	11
5̸	1̸
− 2	7
2	4

2.

dimes	pennies
2	6
−	8

3.

dimes	pennies
6	4
− 5	9

4.
$\begin{array}{r} 28¢ \\ -\ 9¢ \\ \hline \end{array}$

5.
$\begin{array}{r} 92¢ \\ -65¢ \\ \hline \end{array}$

6.
$\begin{array}{r} 75¢ \\ -27¢ \\ \hline \end{array}$

7.
$\begin{array}{r} 33¢ \\ -29¢ \\ \hline \end{array}$

8.
$\begin{array}{r} 34¢ \\ -15¢ \\ \hline \end{array}$

9.
$\begin{array}{r} 84¢ \\ -36¢ \\ \hline \end{array}$

10.
$\begin{array}{r} 50¢ \\ -39¢ \\ \hline \end{array}$

11.
$\begin{array}{r} 51¢ \\ -48¢ \\ \hline \end{array}$

Use with Lesson 11-10, pages 523–524 in the Student Book.
Then go to Lesson 11-11, pages 525–526 in the Student Book.

Add and Subtract Mentally

Name _____

Work from left to right.

Count back by 10s.
Start at 53.
43, 33, 23

$53 - 30 + 3 = ?$

Count on by 1s.
Start at 23.
24, 25, 26

$23 \quad + 3 = 26$

Add and subtract mentally.

1. $55 + 40 - 3 = ?$

$95 \bigcirc 3 = 92$

2. $38 - 2 + 40 = ?$

___ $\bigcirc$ ___ = ___

3. $45 - 20 - 1 = ?$

___ $\bigcirc$ ___ = ___

4. $17 + 30 - 3 = ?$

___ $\bigcirc$ ___ = ___

5. $95 - 10 + 2 = ?$

___ $\bigcirc$ ___ = ___

6. $58 + 10 - 3 = ?$

___ $\bigcirc$ ___ = ___

7. $68 + 30 - 2 = ?$

___ $\bigcirc$ ___ = ___

8. $22 - 20 + 1 = ?$

___ $\bigcirc$ ___ = ___

Use with Lesson 11-11, pages 525–526 in the Student Book.
Then go to Lesson 11-12, pages 529–530 in the Student Book.

one hundred fifty-nine **159**

Balance Number Sentences

Name _____

First solve 13 − 7.
Then find the missing number.

$\underline{13 - 7}$ = $\underline{? + 2}$
↓   ↓
6 = $\underline{④ + 2}$
                ↓
6 = 6

Make each side equal.
Circle the missing number.

1. $\underline{7 + 5}$ = 9 + ?
   ↓
   $\underline{12}$ = $\underline{9 + ③}$
                      ↓
   $\underline{12}$ = $\underline{12}$

---

2. ? + 5 = $\underline{2 + 12}$
              ↓
   $\underline{ + 5}$ = ____
   ↓
   ____ = ____

3. $\underline{7 + 8}$ = 10 + ?
   ↓
   ____ = $\underline{10 + }$
                       ↓
   ____ = ____

---

4. $\underline{16 - 8}$ = ? + 8
   ↓
   ____ = $\underline{ + 8}$
                       ↓
   ____ = ____

5. $\underline{8 + 5}$ = ? + 4
   ↓
   ____ = $\underline{ + 4}$
                       ↓
   ____ = ____

---

6. $\underline{9 - 2}$ = 4 + ?
   ↓
   ____ = $\underline{4 + }$
                     ↓
   ____ = ____

7. $\underline{2 + 5}$ = ? + 3
   ↓
   ____ = $\underline{ + 3}$
                       ↓
   ____ = ____

Use with Lesson 11-12, pages 529–530 in the Student Book.
Then go to Lesson 11-13, pages 531–532 in the Student Book.

Missing Operations

Name _____

Guess and test to find the missing signs.

$$9 \; (?) \; 5 \; (?) \; 4 = 8$$

$$9 \; (+) \; 5 \; (+) \; 4 = 18 \longleftarrow \boxed{18 > 8}$$

$$9 \; (-) \; 5 \; (-) \; 4 = 0 \longleftarrow \boxed{0 < 8}$$

$$9 \; (+) \; 5 \; (-) \; 4 = 10 \longleftarrow \boxed{10 > 8}$$

$$9 \; (-) \; 5 \; (+) \; 4 = 8 \longleftarrow \boxed{8 = 8}$$

Try + and +.
Try − and −.
Try + and −.
Try − and +.

Write the missing signs.

1. $9 \; \bigcirc \; 5 \; \bigcirc \; 8 = 12$

2. $12 \; \bigcirc \; 10 \; \bigcirc \; 2 = 4$

3. $5 \; \bigcirc \; 3 \; \bigcirc \; 9 = 17$

4. $12 \; \bigcirc \; 5 \; \bigcirc \; 3 = 10$

5. $8 \; \bigcirc \; 5 \; \bigcirc \; 3 = 10$

6. $13 \; \bigcirc \; 9 \; \bigcirc \; 8 = 12$

7. $3 \; \bigcirc \; 7 \; \bigcirc \; 2 = 12$

8. $6 \; \bigcirc \; 6 \; \bigcirc \; 8 = 4$

9. $11 \; \bigcirc \; 4 \; \bigcirc \; 7 = 14$

10. $7 \; \bigcirc \; 8 \; \bigcirc \; 8 = 7$

Use with Lesson 11-13, pages 531–532 in the Student Book.
Then go to Lesson 11-14, pages 533–534 in the Student Book.

one hundred sixty-one **161**

Problem-Solving Strategy: Use More Than One Step

Name _____

Read Lily has 75¢.
Tammy gives Lily 13¢.
Lily spends 65¢ on 🥛.
How much money does Lily have now?

Plan Add to find how much Lily has before she buys 🥛.
Subtract the cost of 🥛 from the amount Lily has.

Write

$$75¢ \atop +13¢$$
88¢

$$88¢ \atop -65¢$$
23¢

Lily has 23¢ now.

Check Use real coins to check.

1. Fiona counts 40 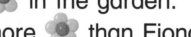 in the garden.
Rudy counts 16 more 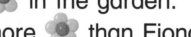 than Fiona.
Fiona picks 10 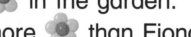 for a bouquet.
How many 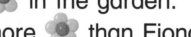 are left in the garden?

_____ are left in the garden.

2. Esther runs for 35 minutes.
Sy runs for 25 minutes.
Then Sy runs for 20 more minutes.
How much longer does
Sy run than Esther?

Sy runs _____ minutes longer than Esther.

Use with Lesson 11-14, pages 533–534 in the Student Book.
Then go to Lesson 11-15, pages 535–536 in the Student Book.

Problem-Solving Applications: Mixed Strategies

Name _____

Read > **Plan** > **Write** > **Check**

Use a strategy you have learned.

Strategy File

Choose the Operation
Guess and Test
Use More Than One Step

1. Yuki counts 24 .
Paul counts 15 more than Yuki.
How many 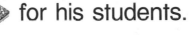 does Paul count?

Paul counts _____ .

2. Mr. Diego needs 29 for his students.
He has only 11 .
How many more does Mr. Diego need?

| 40 | 18 | 8 |

Mr. Diego needs _____ more .

3. Gary has 76¢.
He spends a quarter.
Hans has 52¢.
How much more money does Gary
need to have as much as Hans?

Gary needs _____ to have as much as Hans.

4. Jason has 14 goldfish. His sister
Jessica buys him some more for his
birthday. Now Jason has 27 fish.
How many fish does Jessica buy?

Jessica buys _____ fish.

Use with Lesson 11-15, pages 535–536 in the Student Book.

one hundred sixty-three **163**

Equal Parts

Name _____

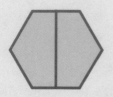 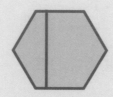

2 equal parts   2 parts not equal

Circle the figure with equal parts.
Then write how many equal parts.

1.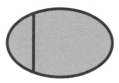

_2_ equal parts

2.

___ equal parts

3.

___ equal parts

4.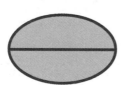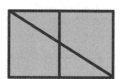

___ equal parts

5.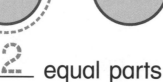

___ equal parts

6.

___ equal parts

7.

___ equal parts

8.

___ equal parts

Use with Lesson 12-1, pages 551–552 in the Student Book.
Then go to Lesson 12-2, pages 553–554 in the Student Book.

One Half, $\frac{1}{2}$

2 equal parts of a whole are called halves	I whole		I of 2 equal parts is $\frac{1}{2}$, or one half

Circle the shapes that show $\frac{1}{2}$.

X the shapes that do not show $\frac{1}{2}$.

1.  2.  3.  4.

5. 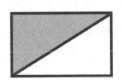 6. 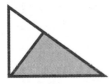 7. 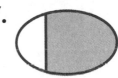 8.

9.  10.  11. 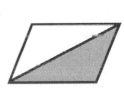 12.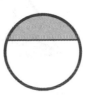

Make halves. Color one half.

Write the fraction for the part you colored.

13.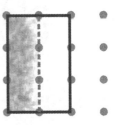

$\dfrac{1}{2}$ part colored / equal parts

14.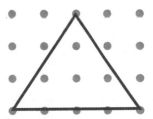

⬚/⬚ part colored / equal parts

15.

⬚/⬚ part colored / equal parts

C Use with Lesson 12-2, pages 553–554 in the Student Book.
C Then go to Lessons 12-3 and 12-4, pages 555–558 in the Student Book. one hundred sixty-five **165**

One Third, $\frac{1}{3}$
One Fourth, $\frac{1}{4}$

Name _____

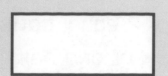

I whole

I of 3 equal parts
is $\frac{1}{3}$, or one third

I of 4 equal parts
is $\frac{1}{4}$, or one fourth

Circle the shapes that show $\frac{1}{3}$.

✗ the shapes that do not show $\frac{1}{3}$.

I.

2.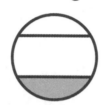

3.

4.

5.

6.

Circle the shapes that show $\frac{1}{4}$.

✗ the shapes that do not show $\frac{1}{4}$.

7.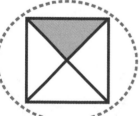

8.

9.

10.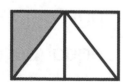

II.

12.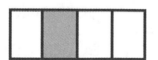

© Use after Lessons 12-3 and 12-4, pages 555–558 in the Student Book.
© Then go to Lesson 12-4A, pages 233–234 in this Workbook.

Part of a Set

Name _____

What part of each set is shaded?

$\dfrac{1}{2}$ part shaded in all $\dfrac{1}{3}$ part shaded in all $\dfrac{1}{4}$ part shaded in all

$\dfrac{1}{2}$ is shaded. $\dfrac{1}{3}$ is shaded. $\dfrac{1}{4}$ is shaded.

What part of each set is shaded?
Write the fraction.

1.

2.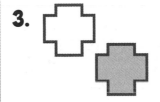

3.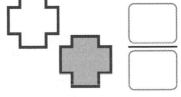

4.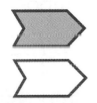

5.

6.

Color one part of each set.
Write the fraction for the part you colored.

7.

8.

9.

10.

11.

12.

Use with Lesson 12-5, pages 559–560 in the Student Book.
Then go to Lessons 12-6 and 12-7, pages 563–566 in the Student Book.

Certain, Possible, Impossible

Name _____

Without looking, is it certain, possible, or impossible to pick a black marble from each bowl?

 certain

 possible

 impossible

Is it certain, possible, or impossible to pick the marble from each bowl? Circle the correct answer.

1. pick a    certain   possible   ⬭impossible⬭

2. pick a   certain   possible   impossible

3. pick a    certain   possible   impossible

4. pick a    certain   possible   impossible

5. pick a    certain   possible   impossible

6. pick a    certain   possible   impossible

Use with Lesson 12-7, pages 565–566 in the Student Book.
Then go to Lesson 12-8, pages 567–568 in the Student Book.

More, Less, or Equally Likely

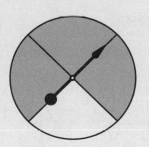 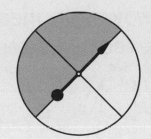 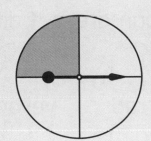

| more likely to land on grey than white | equally likely to land on grey or white | less likely to land on grey than white |

Which color are you more likely to land on?
Write white, grey, or black.

1.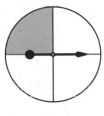

white

2.

_____

3.

_____

Which color are you less likely to land on?

4.

black

5.

_____

6.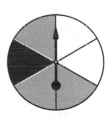

_____

Which color are you more likely to pick?

7.

black

8.

_____

9.

_____

Use with Lesson 12-8, pages 567–568 in the Student Book.
Then go to Lesson 12-9, pages 569–570 in the Student Book.

Arrangements

Name _____

I can dress 4 different ways with these clothes.

 red  yellow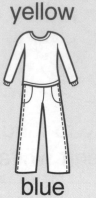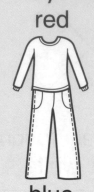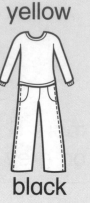

red   red   yellow   yellow

blue   black   blue   black   blue   black

Color to show the different ways you can dress.

1.  purple

blue

grey

white

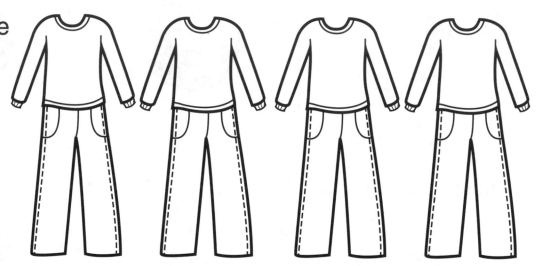

You have 1 yellow, 1 red, and 1 blue bead.
How many different ways can you order the
3 beads? Color to show the different ways.

2.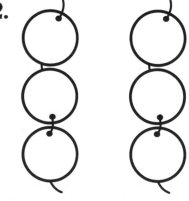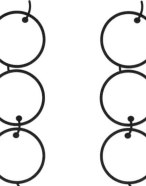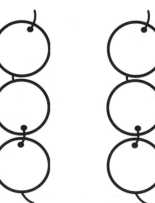

Use with Lesson 12-9, pages 569–570 in the Student Book.
Then go to Lesson 12-10, pages 571–572 in the Student Book.

Problem-Solving Strategy:
Make a Model/Draw a Picture

Name _____

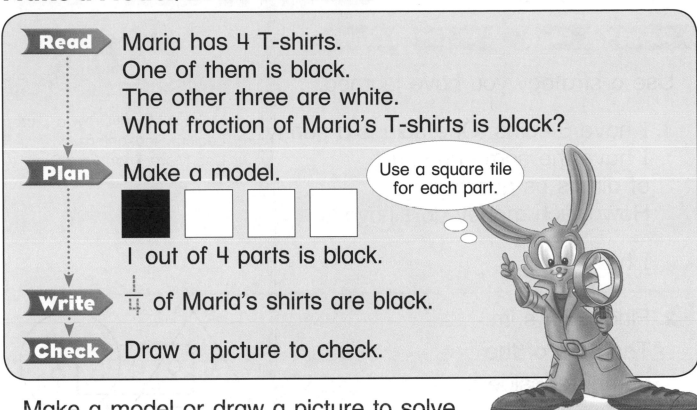

Read ▸ Maria has 4 T-shirts.
One of them is black.
The other three are white.
What fraction of Maria's T-shirts is black?

Plan ▸ Make a model.

Use a square tile for each part.

1 out of 4 parts is black.

Write ▸ $\frac{1}{4}$ of Maria's shirts are black.

Check ▸ Draw a picture to check.

Make a model or draw a picture to solve.

1. There are 5 ✏ in Adam's desk.
4 are blue.
The other is black.
What fraction of the ✏ is black?

$\frac{}{}$ of the ✏ is black.

2. Tim has 9 ⚾ in his bag.
8 ⚾ are new.
1 ⚾ is old.
What fraction of the ⚾ are old?

$\frac{}{}$ ⚾ is old.

3. An 🍎 is divided in 2 equal parts.
One part falls on the floor.
What fraction of the 🍎
falls on the floor?

$\frac{}{}$ of 🍎 fall on the floor.

Use with Lesson 12-10, pages 571–572 in the Student Book.
Then go to Lesson 12-11, pages 573–574 in the Student Book.

Problem-Solving Applications: Mixed Strategies

Name _____

Read ▸ **Plan** ▸ **Write** ▸ **Check**

Use a strategy you have learned.

Strategy File

Make a Model/Draw a Picture
Logical Reasoning
Use More Than One Step

1. I have 5 coins. One coin is a penny.
I have the same number
of dimes as quarters.
How much money do I have?

I have _____.

---

2. Find each sum.
The sum of the
numbers inside the △ is _____.

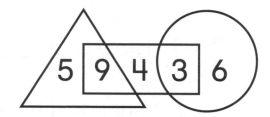

The sum of the numbers not inside the ☐ is _____.

---

3. Penny's ✎ is 7 inches long.
Andrea's ✎ is 1 foot long.
How much longer is Andrea's ✎ ?

Andrea's ✎ is _____ longer.

---

4. Adam, Trey, and Jen play 6 games of ⚽.
Adam wins 3 games. Trey wins 2 games.
Jen wins 1 game. What is the fraction
for the games Jen wins?

Jen wins ☐/☐ of the games.

Use with Lesson 12-11, pages 573–574 in the Student Book.

Additional CCSS Lessons

Pages 175–234 of this workbook have additional lessons with content based on the Common Core State Standards (CCSS). Each lesson has teaching and practice exercises. These lessons can also be found online at progressinmathematics.com. The bottom of the second page of every lesson directs you to another workbook page of more practice of the math taught in the lesson and also to the next *Progress in Mathematics* lesson.

Practice for Additional CCSS Lessons

Pages 236–265 have more practice of the math taught in the additional CCSS lessons. Doing these practice exercises will help you master the work of each additional CCSS lesson more quickly. The bottom of every practice page identifies the lesson that is being reviewed by the workbook exercises, and also identifies the next *Progress in Mathematics* lesson. Before starting a workbook page, read the title. If you need to review the work in that lesson, turn to the page in your workbook where it is taught.

Additional CCSS Lessons

174

Name _____

Objective: To model and write addition sentences for putting together situations

Look at the picture.

Listen to the addition story.

Put together and to model the story.

$$3 + 2 = 5$$

There are 5 sheep on the farm.

Put together  and  to model each addition story.
Write the addition sentence.

1.

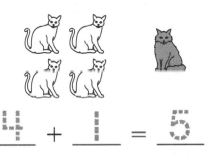

$$\underline{4} + \underline{1} = \underline{5}$$

2.

___ + ___ = ___

3.

___ + ___ = ___

4.

___ + ___ = ___

5. Tell an addition story to go with the model.

Put together  and  to model each addition story.
Write the addition sentence.

6.

___ + ___ = ___

7.

___ + ___ = ___

8.

___ + ___ = ___

9.

___ + ___ = ___

10.

___ + ___ = ___

11.

___ + ___ = ___

Problem Solving Solve. Use a strategy.

12. There are 4 big 🐢 in the barn. There are 2 small 🐢 in the barn. How many 🐢 are in the barn?

____ 🐢

13. Tim has 1 green 🐢. Ann has 4 brown 🐢. How many 🐢 do Tim and Ann have?

____ 🐢

Test Preparation

14. There is 1 pink ❀ in the park. There are 5 white ❀ in the park. Draw to show how many ❀ are in the park. ____ ❀

C For additional Practice, go to page 236 in this Workbook.
C Then go to Lesson 2-3, pages 55–56 in the Student Book.

Equivalent Sums

Chapter 2, Lesson 13A

Objective: To use strategies to find equivalent sums

Use facts you know to help find sums.
Break apart one addend into an addition fact.
Then add the easier facts.

Add 4 + 5.

❶ Break apart 5 to make a double for 4.

$$4 + 5$$
$$4 + 4 + 1$$

❷ Add the doubles.

$$4 + 4 + 1$$
$$8 + 1$$

❸ Then add I more.

$$8 + 1 = 9$$

So, 4 + 5 = 9.

Break apart one addend into an addition fact.
Add the easier facts first. Find the sum.
You can use 🎲 to help.

1. $3 + 4$

$$3 + 3 + 1$$
$$6 + 1 = 7$$

So, 3 + 4 = 7.

2. $7 + 5$

$$7 + \underline{} + 2$$
$$\underline{} + 2 = \underline{}$$

So, 7 + 5 = ___.

Talk It Over

3. How does knowing 6 = 5 + 1 help you solve 5 + 6?

Break apart one addend into an addition fact. Add the easier facts first. Find the sum. You can use  to help.

4. 8 + 4 = ?

___ + ___ + ___ = ___

5. 6 + 5 = ?

___ + ___ + ___ = ___

6. 3 + 2 = ?

___ + ___ + ___ = ___

7. 9 + 3 = ?

___ + ___ + ___ = ___

8. 2 + 9 = ?

___ + ___ + ___ = ___

9. 5 + 4 = ?

___ + ___ + ___ = ___

10. 4 + 7 = ?

___ + ___ + ___ = ___

11. 3 + 8 = ?

___ + ___ + ___ = ___

Problem Solving Solve. Use a strategy.

12. Juan has 4 . Mia has 1 more  than Juan. How many  do Juan and Mia have in all?

____

13. Tilda has 2 . Jaime has 1 more than Tilda. How many do they have in all?

____

What's the Error?

14. Jan added 3 and 4. What error did she make?

3 + 4

3 + 3 + 1

6

So, 3 + 4 = 6.

For additional Practice, go to page 237 in this Workbook.
Then go to Lesson 2-14, pages 81–82 in the Student Book.

Name _____

Objective: To solve word problems with three addends

Marta has 2 .

Joe has 3.

Ana has 1.

How many do they have in all?

Draw a picture or use to solve.

$$2 + 3 + 1 = 6$$

They have 6 in all.

Draw a picture or use.
Write an addition sentence to solve.

1. Mike sees 5.

Elena sees 2.

Rita sees 5.

$$5 + 2 + 5 = 12$$

How many do they see in all? They see 12 in all.

2. There are 7 in the garden.

There are 2 in the yard.

There is 1 in the field. ___ + ___ + ___ = ___

How many are there in all? There are ___ in all.

3. Describe how you added the numbers in exercise 1.

Problem Solving Draw a picture or use 🎲. Write an addition sentence to solve.

4. Sal has 4 blue 🐟 and 2 red 🐟. He also has 2 gold 🐟. How many 🐟 does Sal have in all?

___ + ___ + ___ = ___

Sal has ___ 🐟 in all.

5. Peter finds 3 🐌. Gene finds 1 🐌. Tess finds 6 🐌. How many 🐌 do they find in all?

___ + ___ + ___ = ___

They find ___ 🐌 in all.

6. Marc sees 4 🐸 hopping. He sees 0 🐸 sleeping. He sees 3 🐸 swimming. How many 🐸 does Marc see in all?

Marc sees ___ 🐸 in all.

7. Theo has 8 🦀. Jen has 1 🐱. Steve has 2 🐰. How many pets do they have in all?

They have ___ pets in all.

Critical Thinking

8. Paul draws 4 🐞. Kim draws 3 🐞. Rob draws 1 more 🐞 than Kim. How many 🐞 do they draw in all? Explain how you found your answer.

For additional Practice, go to page 238 in this Workbook.
Then go to Lesson 2-17, pages 87–88 in the Student Book.

Objective: To use models to solve addition problems with unknowns

You can draw ● to find numbers.

$$7 + \underline{\ ?\ } = 10$$

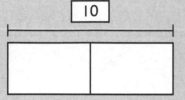

The whole is 10.

Draw 7 to show one part.

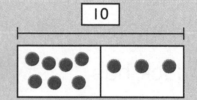

The other part is 3.

$$7 + \underline{\ 3\ } = 10$$

Solve. Draw ● to help.

1. Carla sees 9 🐶 at the park.
   Then more 🐶 come.
   Now 12 🐶 are at the park.
   How many more 🐶 did Carla see?

   Carla saw ___3___ more 🐶.

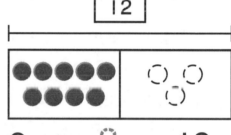

$$9 + \underline{\ 3\ } = 12$$

2. Fran has some 🪙.
   Al has 5 🪙.
   They have 9 🪙 in all.
   How many 🪙 does Fran have?

   Fran has ___ 🪙.

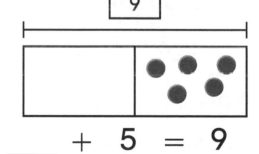

$$\underline{\ \ } + 5 = 9$$

3. Explain how you can find the missing part in addition if you know one part and the whole.

 **Practice**

Problem Solving Solve. Draw ● to help.

4. Jack has 5 🐟 in one bowl.

He has 7 🐟 in another bowl.

How many 🐟 are there in all?

Jack has ____ 🐟 .

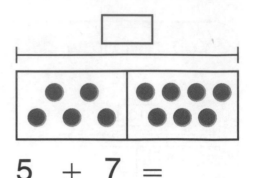

$5 + 7 = $ ____

5. Alicia sees some 🐱.

She also sees 2 🐱 .

She sees 11 cats in all.

How many 🐱 does she see?

Alicia sees ____ 🐱 .

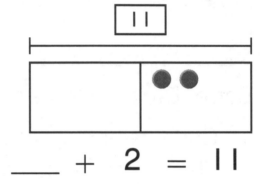

____ $+ 2 = 11$

6. Hugo has 1 🐠.
He buys 8 more 🐠.
How many 🐠 does he
have now?

Hugo has ____ 🐠 now.

7. Jen has 10 🦀 in a box.
Some 🦀 are red.
She has 5 brown 🦀 .
How many 🦀 are red?

Jen has ____ red 🦀 .

Test Preparation

8. Ben has 3 🔤 .
Sue also has some 🔤 .
They have 11 🔤 in all.
How many 🔤 does Sue have?

Explain how you found your answer.

For additional Practice, go to page 239 in this Workbook.
Then go to Lesson 2-18, pages 89–90 in the Student Book.

Name _____

Objective: To use models to solve subtraction problems with unknowns

You can draw ⬤ to find unknown numbers.

$$6 - \underline{\ ?\ } = 4$$

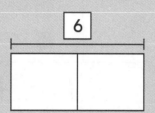

The whole is 6.

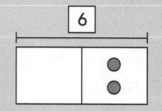

Draw 4 to show one part.

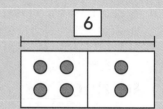

The other part is 2.
$$6 - \underline{\ 2\ } = 4$$

Solve. Draw ⬤ to help.

1. Matt has 4 🍓. He eats some 🍓.

Now Matt has 1 🍓.

How many 🍓 does Matt eat?

Matt eats ___3___ 🍓.

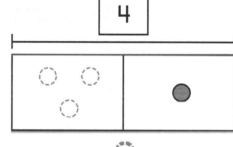

$$4 - \underline{\ 3\ } = 1$$

2. Eva has 5 🍐.

She gives 3 🍐 to Beth.

How many 🍐 does Eva have now?

Eva has ____ 🍐.

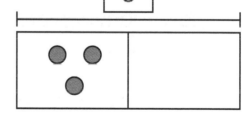

$$5 - 3 = \underline{\ \ \ \ }$$

Talk It Over

3. Explain how you can find the unknown number in a subtraction problem if you know one part and the whole.

Name _____

Problem Solving Solve. Draw ⬤ to help.

4. Teri has some 🍎. She gives
1 🍎 to Fred. Now Teri has
4 🍎. How many 🍎 did
Teri have to start?

Teri had ____ 🍎 to start.

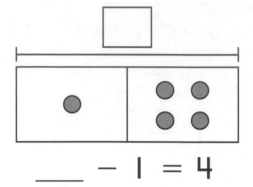

____ – 1 = 4

5. Marc has 6 🍌. He uses
3 🍌 to make bread.
How many 🍌 does Marc
have left?

Marc has ____ 🍌 left.

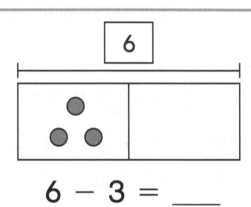

6 – 3 = ____

6. There are 4 ⬤ in a box.
Ted takes 2 ⬤.
How many ⬤ are in the
box now?

There are ____ ⬤ in the box.

7. June has some 🍒. She
gives Mimi 1 🍒. Now June
has 2 🍒. How many 🍒 did
June have to start?

June had ____ 🍒 to start.

Explain Your Reasoning

8. Emilio has 6 🥨. He gives some 🥨 to Lara.
Emilio has no 🥨 left. How many 🥨 did Emilio
give Lara? Explain how you solved the problem.

For additional Practice, go to page 240 in this Workbook.
Then go to Lesson 3-5, pages 109–110 in the Student Book.

Objective: To use related addition and subtraction facts to subtract

Subtract 6 − 4.

Use a related addition fact to help find the difference.

So, 6 − 4 = 2.

Think
? + 4 = 6
2 + 4 = 6

Use a related addition fact to find the difference.
Write the addition fact you use.
Then write the difference.

1. 8 − 5 = ?

_3_ + _5_ = _8_

8 − 5 = _3_

2. 9 − 7 = ?

___ + ___ = ___

9 − 7 = ___

3. 7 − 3 = ?

___ + ___ = ___

7 − 3 = ___

4. 11 − 8 − ?

___ + ___ = ___

11 − 8 = ___

5.   10   10
      − 6   + □   − 6
      ───── ───── ─────
        ?

6.   12   12
      − 3   + □   − 3
      ───── ───── ─────
        ?

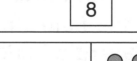

7. What addition fact can you use to solve 8 − 6? Why?

8

● ● ●
● ● ●

Name _____

Use a related addition fact to find the difference.
Write the addition fact you use.

8. 10 − 7 = ___

___ + ___ = ___

9. 6 − 5 = ___

___ + ___ = ___

10. 8 − 4 = ___

___ + ___ = ___

11. 5 − 3 = ___

___ + ___ = ___

12. 7 − 5 = ___

___ + ___ = ___

13. 11 − 6 = ___

___ + ___ = ___

14. 9 [ ]
−3 +[ ]
___   ___

15. 11 [ ]
− 2 +[ ]
___   ___

16. 12 [ ]
− 7 +[ ]
___   ___

Problem Solving Solve. Use a strategy.

17. Lee has 3 fewer ⊂⊃ than Carla. Carla has 8 ⊂⊃. How many ⊂⊃ does Lee have?

___ ⊂⊃

18. Metta has 12 ✏. She gives some ✏ to Ed. Now she has 4 ✏. How many ✏ did Metta give Ed?

___ ✏

Critical Thinking

19. Use the numbers in the box.
Write related addition and subtraction facts.

```
5
9   4
```

___ + ___ = ___   ___ − ___ = ___

For additional Practice, go to page 241 in this Workbook.
Then go to Lesson 3-12, pages 125–126 in the Student Book.

Name _____

Objective: To use bar models to solve addition and subtraction word problems

You can draw ● to solve.
Then write an addition or subtraction sentence.

Stefi has 8 🖊.
She has 6 small 🖊.
The rest are big.

How many big 🖊 does Stefi have?

Stefi has 2 big 🖊.

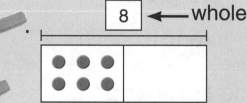

Draw 6 to show one part.

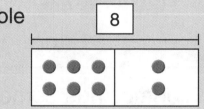

The other part is 2.

$$8 - 6 = 2$$

Solve. Draw ● to help.
Write an addition or subtraction sentence.

1. Justin has 3 blue 🖍. He has 7 red 🖍. How many 🖍 does Justin have?

   Justin has 10 🖍.

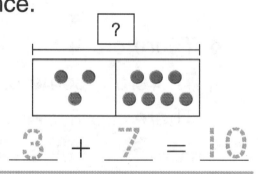

$$\underline{3} + \underline{7} = \underline{10}$$

2. There are 9 📖. Some of the 📖 are open. Five of the 📖 are shut. How many 📖 are open?

   _____ 📖 are open.

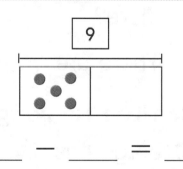

$$\underline{\quad} - \underline{\quad} = \underline{\quad}$$

3. What other number sentence could you use to solve problem 2?

Problem Solving Solve. Draw ● to help.
Write an addition or subtraction sentence.

4. There are 6 .🖌 . Three .🖌
are red. The rest are green.
How many .🖌 are green?

_____ 🖌 are green.

```
            ┌──────6──────┐
            ┌──────┬──────┐
            │ ● ●  │      │
            │  ●   │      │
            └──────┴──────┘
```

_____ − _____ = _____

5. Jamar has some small ⬭.
He has 5 big ⬭. He has
12 ⬭ in all. How many
small ⬭ does Jamar have?

Jamar has _____ small ⬭.

```
            ┌──────12─────┐
            ┌──────┬──────┐
            │      │ ● ● ●│
            │      │ ● ●  │
            └──────┴──────┘
```

_____ + _____ = _____

6. There are 4 pink ✂ .
There are some blue ✂ .
There are 8 ✂ in all.
How many blue ✂ are
there?

There are _____ blue ✂ .

7. Lucy has 11 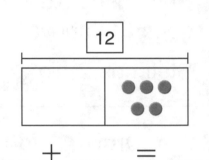.
She fills 5 🥛 with milk.
How many 🥛 are empty?

_____ 🥛 are empty.

Critical Thinking

8. Jorge has 4 . He wants to put
the ✏ into two cups. How many
✏ can he put in his red cup? How
many ✏ can he put in his blue cup?
Explain how you decided.

C For additional Practice, go to page 242 in this Workbook.
C Then go to Lesson 3-13, pages 127–128 in the Student Book.

Name _____

Objective: To ask and answer questions about data in graphs and tally charts

You can ask questions about data in tally charts and graphs.

Think of questions you can answer by using the data in the bar graph.

- How many friends voted for 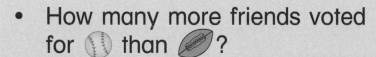?

- How many more friends voted for 🎾 than 🏈?

- How many fewer friends voted for 🏈 than ⚽?

- How many friends voted in all?

How can I use the bar graph to answer the questions?

Use the bar graph to answer the questions.

1. How many more friends like 🎾 than 🏈?

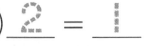 3 ⊖ 2 = 1

2. How many fewer friends like 🏈 than ⚽?

 ___ ◯ ___ = ___

3. How many friends in all voted for a favorite sport?

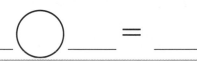 ___ ◯ ___ ◯ ___ = ___

4. What is another question you could answer by reading the bar graph? What is a question that you could not answer?

Use the tally chart to answer the questions.

Molly's Shape Blocks			
Shape	●	■	⬛(trapezoid)
Tally	II	卌 I	III

5. How many fewer  than ■ does Molly have?

_____ ◯ _____ = _____

6. How many shape blocks does Molly have in all?

_____ ◯ _____ ◯ _____ = _____

Problem Solving Use the graph for problems 7 and 8.

7. Will wants to draw the same number of ☾ and ✸. How many more ☾ does he need to draw?

_____ ☾

8. If Will draws another ☆, how many ☆ will he have?

_____ ☆

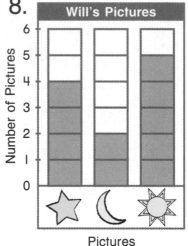

Will's Pictures

Number of Pictures

Pictures

What's the Error?

9. Use the tally chart at the top of the page. John asks Molly how many more ■ than ● she has. Molly says she has 8 more ■. What error did Molly make?

For additional Practice, go to page 243 in this Workbook. Then go to Lesson 4-8, pages 173–174 in the Student Book.

Name _____

Objective: To count, read, and write numerals to 120 and represent a number of objects with a numeral

▶ You can write numbers 100 through 120 using one hundred, tens, and ones.

hundreds	tens	ones

1 hundred 1 ten 2 ones
112
one hundred twelve

▶ Count in order from 100 to 112.

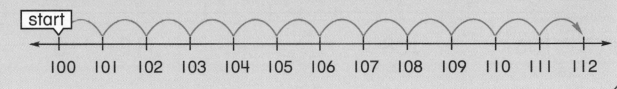

start

100 101 102 103 104 105 106 107 108 109 110 111 112

Use the model to write how many.

1.

hundreds	tens	ones

___1___ hundred ___0___ tens ___5___ ones

___105___

2.

hundreds	tens	ones

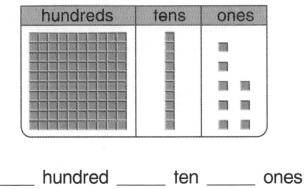

_____ hundred _____ ten _____ ones

_____

Talk It Over

3. Count aloud from 100 to 120. Do you say more or fewer numbers when you count from 10 to 20?

Use the model to write how many.

4.	hundreds	tens	ones

_____ hundred _____ ten _____ ones

_____

5.	hundreds	tens	ones

_____ hundred _____ tens _____ ones

_____

Count by ones. Write the missing numbers.

6.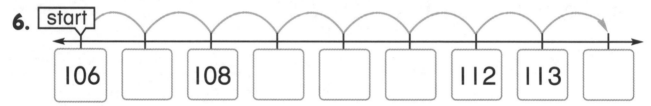

start							
106		108				112	113	

7.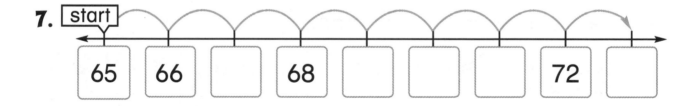

start							
65	66		68				72	

8.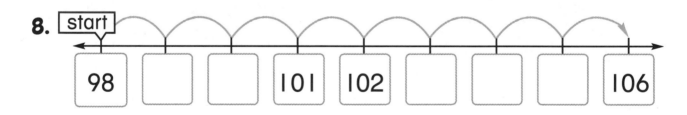

start							
98			101	102			106

Explain Your Reasoning

9. When you count by ones, what number 「 118, 119, 120, ? 」 comes after 120? Explain how you know.

For additional Practice, go to page 244 in this Workbook.
Then go to Lesson 5-8, pages 211–212 in the Student Book.

Name _____

Properties of Operations
Chapter 6, Lesson 2A

Objective: To apply the properties of operations as strategies to add

When you change the order of the addends, the sum is the same.

If you know that
9 + 5 = 14,

If you know
$$\begin{array}{r} 7 \\ +\ 3 \\ \hline 10 \end{array}$$

you also know that
5 + 9 = 14.

you also know
$$\begin{array}{r} 3 \\ +\ 7 \\ \hline 10 \end{array}$$

Find the sum. Change the order of the addends.
Find the sum again.

1.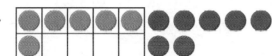

6 + 7 = 13

7 + 6 = 13

2.

___ + ___ = ___

___ + ___ = ___

3. Explain why you can change the order of
the addends without changing the sum.

Name _____

Practice

Find the sum.
Change the order of the addends.
Find the sum again.

Use a  and ● to help.

4. 4 + 7 = ___

___ + ___ = ___

5. 6 + 9 = ___

___ + ___ = ___

6. 8 + 5 = ___

___ + ___ = ___

7. 7 + 8 = ___

___ + ___ = ___

8. 9
   +4   +☐
   ___   ___
   ☐   ☐

9. 8
   +6   +☐
   ___   ___
   ☐   ☐

10. 9
   +3   +☐
   ___   ___
   ☐   ☐

11. 7
   +9   +☐
   ___   ___
   ☐   ☐

12. 6
   +5   +☐
   ___   ___
   ☐   ☐

13. 3
   +8   +☐
   ___   ___
   ☐   ☐

 **Problem Solving** Solve. Use a strategy.

14. June writes an addition sentence with a sum of 16. When she changes the order of the addends, her addition sentences are exactly the same. What addition sentences does Jane write?

___ + ___ = ___

___ + ___ = ___

Test Preparation

15. Write two addition sentences that use the same addends and have the same sum.

___ + ___ = ___

___ + ___ = ___

194 Grade 1, Lesson 6-2A

For additional Practice, go to page 245 in this Workbook.
Then go to Lesson 6-3, pages 261–262 in the Student Book.

Name _____

Objective: To make 10 to find equivalent sums

You can make 10 to help find sums.
Break apart one addend into two parts.
Make 10. Then find the sum.

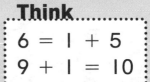

Think
$6 = 1 + 5$
$9 + 1 = 10$

Add: $9 + 6$

❶ Break apart 6 $9 +$ 6
to make 10.
$9 + 1 + 5$

❷ Add to make 10. $9 + 1 + 5$
$10 + 5$

❸ Then add 5 more. $10 + 5 = 15$

So, $9 + 6 = 15$.

Break apart one addend into two parts.
Make 10. Then find the sum.

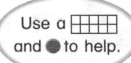
Use a ▦
and ● to help.

1. $8 + 5 = ?$

$8 + 2 + 3 = ?$

$10 + 3 = 13$

So, $8 + 5 = 13$.

2. $7 + 4 = ?$

$7 + \_\_ + 1 = ?$

$\_\_ + 1 = \_\_$

So, $7 + 4 = \_\_$.

3. Explain how you would make 10
to find the sum for $8 + 4$.

Name _____

Practice

Break apart one addend into two parts. Make
10. Find the sum. You can use ⚫ to help.

4. 9 + 3 = ?

___ + ___ + ___ = ___

5. 7 + 8 = ?

___ + ___ + ___ = ___

6. 4 + 9 = ?

___ + ___ + ___ = ___

7. 6 + 7 = ?

___ + ___ + ___ = ___

8. 5 + 7 = ?

___ + ___ + ___ = ___

9. 8 + 9 = ?

___ + ___ + ___ = ___

10. 6 + 8 = ?

___ + ___ + ___ = ___

11. 9 + 7 = ?

___ + ___ + ___ = ___

Problem Solving Solve. Use a strategy.

12. Mario has 5 .
Ella has 8 .
How many more
does Ella have than Mario?

____

13. Ms. Ruiz has 11 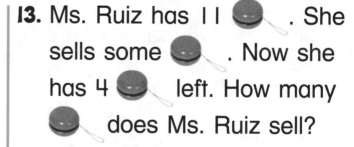. She
sells some . Now she
has 4 left. How many
 does Ms. Ruiz sell?

____

What's the Error?

14. Luis added 9 and 5. What error
did he make?

9 + 5
9 + 1 + 3
   10 + 3 = 13
So, 9 + 5 = 13

For additional Practice, go to page 246 in this Workbook.
Then go to Lesson 6-4, pages 263–264 in the Student Book.

Name _____

Objective: To make 10 to help with subtraction from numbers greater than 10

You can make 10 to help subtract.

- Break apart the number subtracted into two parts.
- Subtract one part from the whole to make 10.
- Then subtract the other part.

Subtract: $14 - 6$

❶ Start with 14.
Break apart 6.
Subtract 4
to make 10.

❷ Then subtract
2 more.

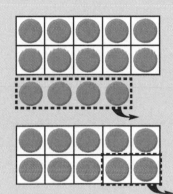

$14 - 6$

$14 - 4 - 2$

$10 - 2 = 8$

So, $14 - 6 = 8$.

Subtract one part from the whole to make 10.
Then subtract the other part.

Use a ▦
and ● to help.

1. $15 - 9$

$15 - \underline{5} - \underline{4}$

$\underline{10} - \underline{4} = \underline{6}$

So, $15 - 9 = \underline{6}$.

2. $16 - 7$

$16 - \underline{} - \underline{}$

$\underline{10} - \underline{} = \underline{}$

So, $16 - 7 = \underline{}$.

Talk It Over

3. Explain how you would make 10 to find the
difference of $14 - 9$.

Name _____

Subtract one part from the whole to make 10.
Then subtract the other part.

Use a ▢▢▢▢
and ● to help.

4. 17 − 8

_____

5. 13 − 9

_____

6. 15 − 7

_____

7. 16 − 8

_____

8. 18 − 9

_____

9. 14 − 7

_____

10. 13 − 6

_____

11. 13 − 8

_____

 **Problem Solving** Solve. Use a strategy.

12. Al has 6 fewer 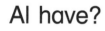 than

Jean. Jean has 15 .

How many ● does

Al have?

_____ ●

13. There were 17 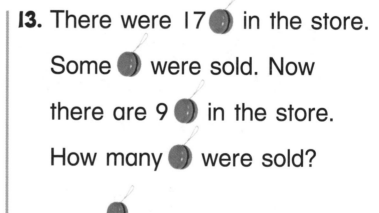 in the store.

Some ● were sold. Now

there are 9 ● in the store.

How many ● were sold?

_____ ●

Critical Thinking

14. Explain why you cannot make 10
     to subtract 16 − 3.

C For additional Practice, go to page 247 in this Workbook.
C Then go to Lesson 6-8, pages 273–274 in the Student Book.

Objective: To understand the meaning of the equals sign and to determine if an equation is true or false

A number sentence can be true or false.

▶ A number sentence is **true** when both sides of the equals sign make the same number.

| = means |
| is the same as |

A number sentence is **false** when both sides of the equals sign do not make the same number.

Is 7 + 6 = 13 true or false? | Is 14 − 8 = 7 true or false?

Add to check.
    7 + 6 = 13
  Does 13 = 13? Yes.
So, 7 + 6 = 13 is true.

Subtract to check.
    14 − 8 = 6
  Does 6 = 7? No.
So, 14 − 8 = 7 is false.

Circle the number sentences that are true.
Cross out the number sentences that are false.

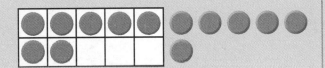

1. 13 = 8 + 5   **2.** 10 − 6 = 3   **3.** 15 = 15

4. 14 − 5 = 10   **5.** 3 − 1 = 10 − 8   **6.** 1 + 4 = 4 + 1

7. How can you check if a number sentence is true or false?

Circle the number sentences that are true.
Cross out the number sentences that are false.

8. $10 = 7 + 3$ **9.** $9 + 5 = 16$ **10.** $3 + 7 = 5 + 5$

11. $4 + 0 = 13 - 9$ **12.** $7 + 8 = 15$ **13.** $20 - 10 = 5$

14. $18 = 18$ **15.** $17 = 1 + 7$ **16.** $4 + 3 + 4 = 11$

17. $16 - 7 = 15 - 6$ **18.** $19 = 9 + 10$ **19.** $8 - 3 = 3 + 8$

Problem Solving Solve. Use a strategy.

20. Paulo has 9 big 🚗. He has the same number of small 🚗 as big 🚗. How many 🚗 does Paulo have in all?

____◯____ = ____

Paulo has ____ in all.

21. Allie has 11 toy 🦖. Some 🦖 are green. Five 🦖 are brown. How many 🦖 are green?

____◯____ = ____

____ are green.

Critical Thinking

Show two ways to make each number sentence true.

22. $9 + 9 = $ ____

$9 + 9 = $ ____

23. $6 + 3 + 4 = $ ____

$6 + 3 + 4 = $ ____

24. ____ $= 7 - 7$

____ $= 7 - 7$

For additional Practice, go to page 248 in this Workbook.
Then go to Lesson 6-11, pages 281–282 in the Student Book.

Name _____

 Add and Subtract to Compare
Chapter 6, Lesson 11A

Objective: To use pictures and equations to solve comparison problems with the unknowns in any position

You can add and subtract to compare.

Greta has 13 toys. Greta has 6 more toys than Sam. How many toys does Sam have?

Draw ○ to compare.   6 more

Greta | ○○○○○○○○○○○○○

Sam | ○○○○○○○

$$13 - 6 = 7$$

Sam has 7 toys.

Draw ○ to compare. Then add or subtract to solve.

1. Amy has 9 stickers. Gina has 4 more stickers than Amy. How many stickers does Gina have?

Amy | ○○○○○○○○○

Gina | ○○○○○○○○○○○○○

$$9 + 4 = 13$$

Gina has 13 stickers.

2. Floyd wins 14 tops. Sue wins 8 tops. How many fewer tops does Sue win?

Floyd |

Sue |

___ − ___ = ___

Sue wins ____ fewer tops.

3. Explain how subtraction can help you compare numbers.

Problem Solving Draw ○ to compare.
Then add or subtract to solve.

4. Rob has 12 pens.
He has 7 more pens than
Ally. How many pens does
Ally have?

Rob	
Ally	

____ − ____ = ____

Ally has ____ pens.

5. Sally has 6 beads. Mae has
9 more beads than Sally.
How many beads does
Mae have?

Sally	
Mae	

____ + ____ = ____

Mae has ____ beads.

6. Ben has 9 pens. Allen has
7 more pens than Ben. How
many pens does Allen have?

____ pens

7. Jo sold 17 hats. She sold
10 fewer ribbons. How
many ribbons did Jo sell?

____ ribbons

What's the Error?

8. Beth writes 10 − 7 = 3 to solve this
problem. She says Ely has 3 tops.
What error did Beth make?

Kyle has 10 tops.
He has 7 fewer tops
than Ely. How many
tops does Ely have?

For additional Practice, go to page 249 in this Workbook.
Then go to Lesson 6-12, pages 283–284 in the Student Book.

Objective: To distinguish between attributes of plane figures and draw them based on defining attributes

Tim draws a figure. Circle the words that tell you that Tim draws a triangle.

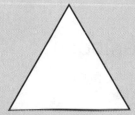

(3 sides)   white

(3 corners)   small

The number of sides and the number of corners tell about the kind of figure.
The color and size do not.

Circle the words that tell about the kind of figure.
Then draw the figure.

1. pentagon	red	2. circle	0 corners
	5 sides		small

3. square	big	4. triangle	green
	4 corners		3 sides

5. Explain how you can tell if a figure is a rectangle.
Does the color or the size matter?

Practice

Circle the words that tell about the kind of figure.
Then draw the figure.

6. circle	gray	**7.** triangle	turned
	0 sides		3 corners

8. rectangle	tall	**9.** pentagon	blue
	4 sides		5 corners

 **Problem Solving** Solve. Use a strategy.

10. Marco draws a figure with fewer than 3 corners. Lisa draws a figure with the same number of corners as a square. Kayla draws a figure with 3 sides.

Which figure does each child draw?

_____ _____ _____

11. Sally uses these clues to draw a plane figure.

- It is small.
- It has 5 sides.
- It is gray.

Circle Sally's figure. Explain how you decided.

For additional Practice, go to page 250 in this Workbook.
Then go to Lesson 7-3, pages 301–302 in the Student Book.

Name _____

Objective: To compose two-dimensional shapes using triangles, rectangles, squares, and parts of circles

Step 1: Put together two plane figures to make a new figure.

Start with 2 quarter circles.   Make a half circle.

Step 2: Put together two of the new figure from step 1 to make other shapes.

Use 2 half circles.   Make a new shape.

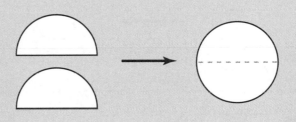

a. Draw lines to show how to use the plane figures to make a new figure. **b.** Draw to show how to use two of the new figure to make another shape.

1. a.  **b.**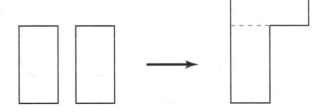

2. a. 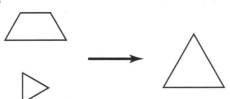 **b.**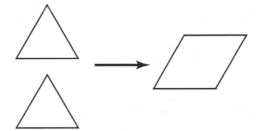

 Talk It Over

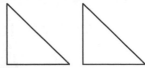

3. Explain how to use 2 triangles to make a square.

Name _____

a. Draw lines to show how to use the plane figures to make a new figure.

b. Draw to show how to use two of the new figure to make another shape.

4. a.    **b.**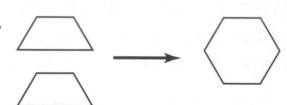

5. a. 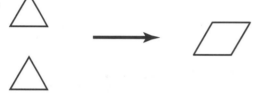   **b.**

6. a. 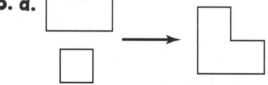   **b.**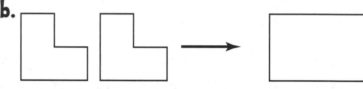

Problem Solving   Solve. Use a strategy.

7. Bria uses 2 △ to make a ▱.
Then she uses 3 ▱ to make a hexagon.
Draw lines to show how Bria makes the
hexagon.

Critical Thinking

8. Draw 4 shapes that could make
this rectangle.

For additional Practice, go to page 251 in this Workbook.
Then go to Lesson 7-4, pages 303–304 in the Student Book.

Name _____

Objective: To compose three-dimensional figures using cubes, rectangular prisms, cones, and cylinders

Step 1: Put together two solid figures to make a new solid figure.

 and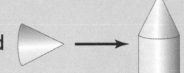

Step 2: Use the new figure from Step 1 to make other shapes.

and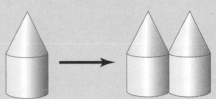

a. Use the two solid figures. Circle the new figure you can make.

b. Use two of the new figure from a. Circle the shape you can make.

1. a.

 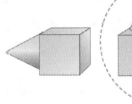 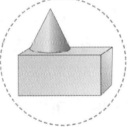 

1. b.

 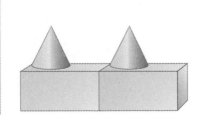 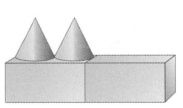 

2. Can you combine 2 cylinders to make a rectangular prism? Why or why not?

a. Use the two solid figures. Circle the new figure you can make.

b. Use two of the new figure from a. Circle the shape you can make.

3. a.

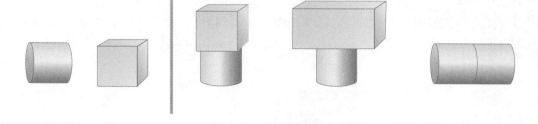

3. b.

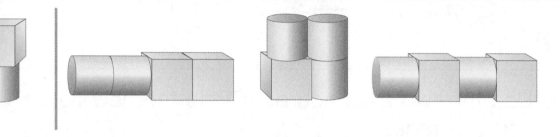

Critical Thinking

4. Vin uses 3 cubes to make this figure. Then he uses the figure to make other shapes.

a. Circle the new figures Vin could make.

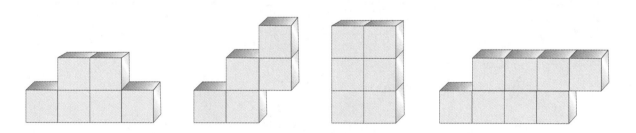

b. Explain how Vin uses his figure with 3 cubes to make new figures.

For additional Practice, go to page 252 in this Workbook.
Then go to Lesson 7-6, pages 309–310 in the Student Book.

Name _____

Objective: To measure the distance along a two-segment path using nonstandard units

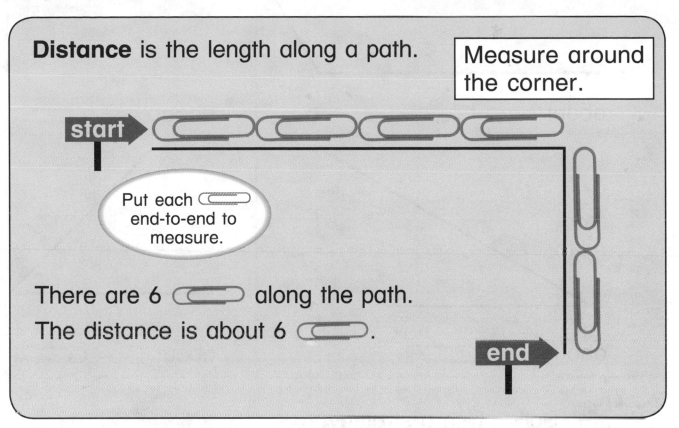

Distance is the length along a path.

Measure around the corner.

start ▶

Put each ⬭ end-to-end to measure.

There are 6 ⬭ along the path.

The distance is about 6 ⬭.

end ▶

Use ⬭ to measure the distance along each path.

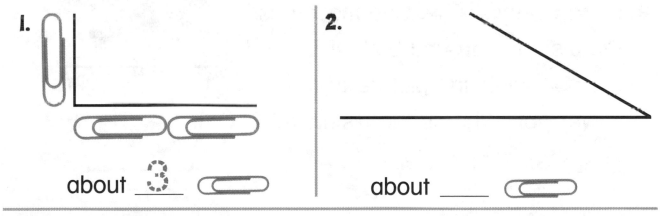

I.

about __3__ ⬭

2.

about ____ ⬭

3. Describe how to measure the distance along a path.

Use 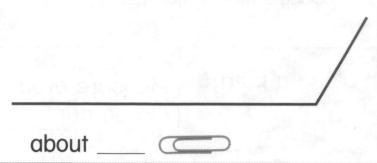 to measure the distance along each path.

4.

about ____ ⬭

5.

about ____ ⬭

6.

about ____ ⬭

7.

about ____ ⬭

Problem Solving Solve. Use a strategy.

8. Mara uses ⬭. She measures the distance around both sides and the bottom of the picture of the flower pot. What is the distance?

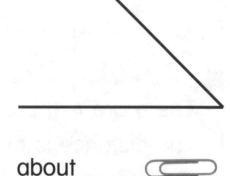

about ____ ⬭

What's the Error?

9. Joel says the distance along the path is about 4 ⬭. What error did he make?

For additional Practice, go to page 253 in this Workbook.
Then go to Lesson 9-2, pages 409–410 in the Student Book.

Name _____

Objective: To compare the lengths of two objects indirectly by using a third object

You can compare the lengths of two objects by using another object.

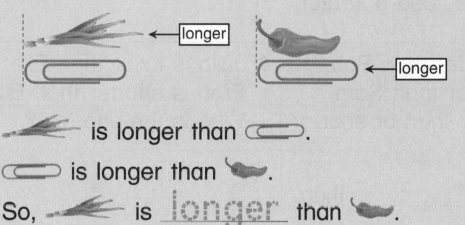

Which is longer?
Use a ⬭.
Compare it to each object to decide.

🌿 is longer than ⬭.

⬭ is longer than 🌶.

So, 🌿 is __longer__ than 🌶.

Compare the length of each picture to a small ⬭.
Write **shorter** or **longer** to finish each sentence.

1. 🌿 is _____ than 🫛 .

2. 🥕 is _____ than 🌭 .

3. 🍄 is _____ than 🥒 .

4. How can you compare the lengths of two objects that are not side by side?

Compare the length of each picture in the box to a small 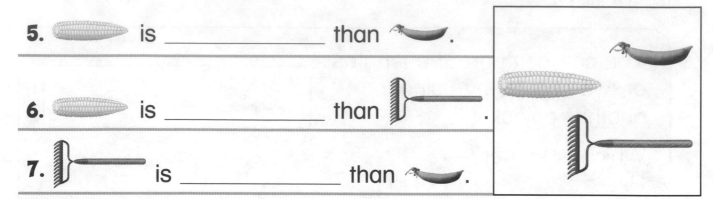.
Write **shorter** or **longer** to finish each sentence.

5. is _____ than .

6. is _____ than .

7. is _____ than .

Problem Solving Solve. Use a strategy.

8. Mary is shorter than Bob.
Bob is shorter than Sam.
Is Sam taller than or shorter than Mary?

Sam is _____ than Mary.

9. Julio is taller than Elle.
Fran is shorter than Elle.
Who is the shortest?

_____

Test Preparation

10. Compare each picture to a small .

Write **shorter** or **longer** to finish each sentence.

a. The is _____ than the .

b. The is _____ than the .

For additional Practice, go to page 254 in this Workbook.
Then go to Lesson 9-4B, pages 213–214 in this Workbook.

Name _____

Objective: To use a ruler with nonstandard units to measure length

► Make a ruler.

① Line up small paper clips along a strip of paper.

② Mark the paper at the end of each paper clip.

③ Number the marks. Each mark on the ruler means 1 unit.

► Use the marks on your ruler to measure small objects.

The peapod is about 2 units long.

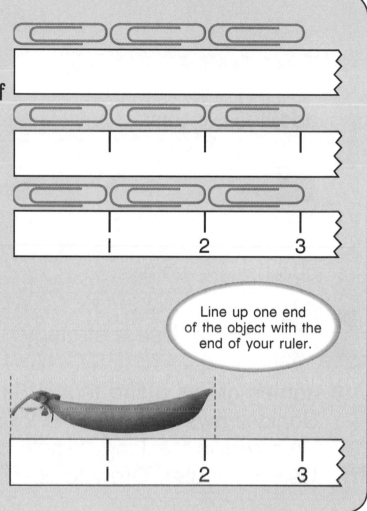

Line up one end of the object with the end of your ruler.

Use your ruler to measure the length of each picture.

1.
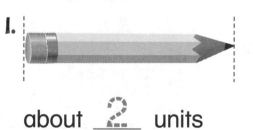

about __2__ units

2.
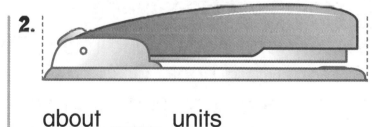

about ____ units

Talk It Over

3. Explain how to use a ruler to find the length of an object.

Use your ruler to measure the length of each picture.

4.

about ____ units

5.

about ____ units

6.

about ____ units

7. GLUE

about ____ units

 **Problem Solving** Solve. Use a strategy.

8. James draws a line that is 5 units long.
Sonia draws a line that is 2 units long.
Who draws the longer line? How much longer?
Use your ruler. Draw to solve.

_____ draws the longer line. It is ____ units longer.

Explain Your Reasoning

9. Cara and Andy made rulers. They measure a book. Cara says the book is 5 units long. Andy says it is 6 units long. Why are their answers different?

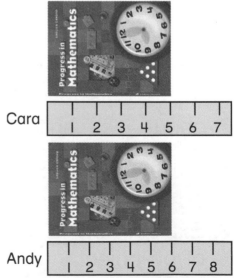

Cara

Andy

For additional Practice, go to page 255 in this Workbook.
Then go to Lesson 9-5, pages 415–416 in the Student Book.

Objective: To add 2 two-digit numbers using drawings

The soccer team scored 26 goals last year.
This year they scored 31 goals. How many goals
did the team score altogether in both years?

$26 + 31 = ?$

Draw the addends.　　Add the ones.　　Then add the tens.

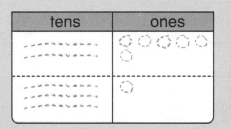

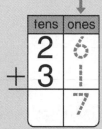

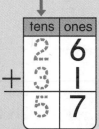

The drawing shows a total of 5 tens and 7 ones.
The team scored 57 goals altogether in both years.

Add. Draw tens and ones to help.

1.

tens	ones
3	2
+ 2	4

tens	ones

2.

tens	ones
4	5
+ 1	3

tens	ones

3.

tens	ones
2	0
+ 2	7

tens	ones

4.

tens	ones
1	1
+ 6	8

tens	ones

5. Tell how you use drawings to help
you add tens and ones.

Add. Draw tens and ones to help.

6.

tens	ones
3	4
+ 1	3

tens	ones

7.

tens	ones
2	8
+ 4	0

tens	ones

8.

tens	ones
5	4
+ 2	5

tens	ones

9.

tens	ones
6	1
+ 3	7

tens	ones

 Problem Solving Solve. Use a strategy.

10. Mary has 23 stickers. Joe has 2 more stickers than Mary. How many stickers do they have in all?

____ stickers

11. Emily wins 38 tickets. Louis wins 7 fewer tickets than Emily. How many tickets do they win altogether?

____ tickets

Test Preparation

12a. Karen scores 21 points in a game. Debby scores 4 more points than Karen. How many points does Debby score?

_____

12b. In the same game, Ani scores 3 more points than Debby. How many points does Ani score?

_____

12c. How many points did the three girls score in all?

_____

For additional Practice, go to page 256 in this Workbook.
Then go to Lesson 10-3, pages 469–470 in the Student Book.

Objective: To count on by tens or ones from a two-digit number to add

You can count on to add.

What is 3 more than 26?	What is 30 more than 26?
Start at 26. Count on 3 ones.	Start at 26. Count on 3 tens.

3 = 3 ones

30 = 3 tens

+1 +1 +1
26, 27, 28, 29

+10 +10 +10
26, 36, 46, 56

29 is 3 more than 26.	56 is 30 more than 26.

Model each number. Count on by ones
to find the number that is more.

1. 2 more than 17

2. 3 more than 24

_____

3. 1 more than 45

_____

Model each number. Count on by tens
to find the number that is more.

4. 30 more than 28

5. 20 more than 15

_____

6. 10 more than 37

_____

7. Explain how to count on to find 30 more than 23.

Name _____

Count on by ones to find the number that is more.
Use ▦▦▦▦▦ and ▪ to check.

8. 3 more than 52

_____

9. I more than 74

_____

10. 2 more than 85

_____

II. I more than 48

_____

12. 4 more than 32

_____

13. 3 more than 60

_____

Count on by tens to find the number that is more.
Use ▦▦▦▦▦ and ▪ to check.

14. 20 more than 41

_____

15. 30 more than 54

_____

16. 10 more than 89

_____

17. 40 more than 13

_____

18. 20 more than 70

_____

19. 30 more than 39

_____

 **Problem Solving** Solve. Use a strategy.

20. Paul sees 42 kites. Alicia sees 3 more kites than Paul sees. How many kites does Alicia see?

Alicia sees _____ kites.

21. Kayla jumps II times. She jumps 20 more times. Then she jumps 3 more times. How many times does Kayla jump in all?

Kayla jumps _____ times.

What's the Error?

22. Tia says that 3 more than 59 is 61.
What error did she make?

For additional Practice, go to page 257 in this Workbook.
Then go to Lesson 10-5, pages 473–474 in the Student Book.

Name _____

Objective: To use strategies to add one-digit numbers or multiples of 10 to two-digit numbers

Use different strategies to add.

Count On to Add	Break Apart to Add

Count On to Add

$30 + 28 = ?$

❶ Change the order of the addends if you need to.

❷ Then count on by tens.

$$\begin{array}{cc} 30 & 28 \\ +28 & +30 \\ \hline ? & 58 \end{array}$$

+10 +10 +10
28, 38, 48, 58

$30 + 28 = 58$
$28 + 30 = 58$

Break Apart to Add

$42 + 7 = ?$

❶ Break apart one addend into tens and ones.

❷ Add the ones.

❸ Then add the tens.

$$42 \rightarrow \begin{array}{c} 40 \\ 2 \end{array}$$

$$\begin{array}{ccccc} 42 & 40 & 40 & & \\ & 2 & 2 & 40 \\ +7 & +7 & +7 & +9 \\ \hline ? & ? & ? & 49 \end{array}$$

$42 + 7 = 49$

Count on to add.

1.
$$\begin{array}{cc} 20 & 19 \\ +19 & +20 \\ \hline ? & 39 \end{array}$$

Break apart to add.

2.
$$33 \rightarrow \begin{array}{c} 30 \\ 3 \end{array}$$

$$\begin{array}{ccc} 33 & 30 & 30 \\ +5 & +5 & +8 \\ \hline & & 38 \end{array}$$

3. Explain how you could add 52 and 6.

Name _____

Use a strategy to find the sum.

4.
```
  30
+ 48
```

5.
```
  20
+ 63
```

6.
```
  24
+  5
```

7.
```
  73
+  6
```

8.
```
  41
+  7
```

9.
```
  60
+ 16
```

10.
```
  54
+  5
```

11.
```
  20
+ 59
```

12.
```
  82
+  6
```

13.
```
  26
+ 12
```

14.
```
  77
+  2
```

 Solve. Use a strategy.

15. Elio has 3 dimes. He finds 19¢.

Now Elio has ____.

16. Jared has 23¢. Marta has 6 pennies.

Jared and Marta have ____.

Critical Thinking

17. Jan added to find 56 + 23 = 79. She says that 23 + 56 = 80. Which number sentence is false? How do you know?

For additional Practice, go to page 258 in this Workbook.
Then go to Lesson 10-5B, pages 221–222 in this Workbook.

Objective: To use strategies to add two 2-digit numbers

Use strategies to add. $25 + 32 = ?$

One Way to Add	Another Way to Add
❶ Break apart one addend into tens and ones.	❶ Break apart both addends into tens and ones.
❷ Count on by tens.	❷ Add the tens.
❸ Count on by ones.	❸ Add the ones.
	❹ Add the sums.

One Way:
$$\begin{array}{c} 25 \\ + \boxed{32} \\ \hline ? \end{array} \quad \begin{array}{c} 25 \\ \boxed{30} \\ + \boxed{2} \\ \hline ? \end{array} \rightarrow \boxed{55} \quad \begin{array}{c} +\ 2 \\ \hline \boxed{57} \end{array}$$

Another Way:
$$25 \rightarrow \boxed{20} + \boxed{5}$$
$$+ 32 \rightarrow + \boxed{30} + \boxed{2}$$
$$\overline{} \qquad \overline{50 + 7 = 57}$$

So, $25 + 32 = 57$

Break apart one addend. Add.

1.

$$\begin{array}{c} 46 \\ + \boxed{17} \end{array} \quad \begin{array}{c} \boxed{46} \\ \boxed{10} \\ + \boxed{7} \end{array} \rightarrow \boxed{56} \quad \begin{array}{c} + \boxed{7} \\ \hline 63 \end{array}$$

Break apart both addends. Add.

2.

$$61 \rightarrow \boxed{60} + \boxed{1}$$
$$+19 \rightarrow + \boxed{10} + \boxed{9}$$
$$\overline{70 + 10 = \underline{80}}$$

Talk It Over

3. Explain two different ways to add 37 and 42.

$$37 + 42 = ?$$

Name _____

Use a strategy to find the sum.

4.   28
  + 14

5.   55
  + 23

6.   36
  + 24

7.   73
  + 13

8.   58
  + 31

9.   15
  + 49

10.   67
  + 24

11.   62
  + 16

12.   21
  + 63

 **Problem Solving** Solve. Use a strategy.

13. Alma has some party hats. 17 hats are pink. 15 hats are blue. How many hats does Alma have?

Alma has ____ party hats.

14. Jamal has 39 party stickers. Ed has 11 more stickers than Jamal. How many stickers does Ed have?

Ed has ____ party stickers.

Test Preparation

15. What is the missing addend? Explain how you found the answer.

   43
  + ?
  ―――
  90

For additional Practice, go to page 259 in this Workbook. Then go to Lesson 10-6, pages 475–476 in the Student Book.

Objective: To use bar models to solve addition problems with sums to 100

The team has 18 girls. The team has 17 boys.
How many children are on the team?

$18 + 17 = ?$

Use a bar model to help.
One part is 18.
The other part is 17.
Find the whole.

?	
18	17

Add to solve.

$$\begin{array}{r} 18 \\ +17 \\ \hline 35 \end{array}$$

There are 35 children on the team.

Complete the bar model. Add to solve.

1. A store has 36 soccer balls.
The store has 12 more footballs
than soccer balls. How many
footballs does the store have?

_____ footballs

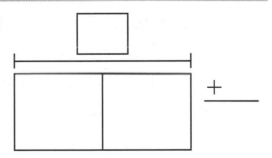
$\begin{array}{r} \\ + \\ \hline \end{array}$

2. Greg played for 45 minutes. Then
played for 25 minutes more. How
many minutes did he play in all?

_____ minutes

$\begin{array}{r} \\ + \\ \hline \end{array}$

3. How can a bar model help you solve an
addition problem?

Name _____

Problem Solving Complete the bar model. Add to solve.

4. Marty scores 29 points in a computer game. His friend scores 21 points. How many points do they score in all?

_____ points

$+$ _____

5. Jay's team swims 23 laps. Ann's team swims 20 more laps than Jay's. How many laps does Ann's team swim?

_____ laps

$+$ _____

6. Ms. Ruiz sells some flags at the game. She sells 47 red flags. She sells 39 green flags. How many flags does Ms. Ruiz sell?

_____ flags

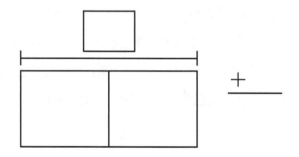

$+$ _____

7. Tom bowls 28 games. He bowls 8 fewer games than Angie. How many games does Angie bowl?

_____ games

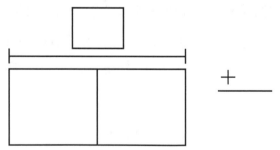

$+$ _____

Critical Thinking

8. Joy bought a water bottle for 35¢. Now she has 58¢. How much money did she have to start? _____ ¢

C For additional Practice, go to page 260 in this Workbook.
C Then go to Lesson 10-11, pages 487–488 in the Student Book.

Name _____

Objective: To find mentally, without having to count, 10 more or 10 less

Ray writes a number 10 less than 42.
Liz writes a number 10 more than 42.
What numbers do Ray and Liz write?

Find the number that is 10 less than 42.	Find the number that is 10 more than 42.
Start at 42. Count back 10.	Start at 42. Count on 10.

32 is 10 less than 42. Ray writes the number 32.	52 is 10 more than 42. Liz writes the number 52.

Use mental math. Write the number that is 10 more.

1. 15 _25_ | **2.** 31 ____ | **3.** 86 ____ | **4.** 53 ____

Use mental math. Write the number that is 10 less.

5. ____ 36 | **6.** ____ 67 | **7.** ____ 74 | **8.** ____ 80

9. Explain how you can find the number that is 10 less than 18.

Use mental math.
Write the number that is 10 less
and the number that is 10 more.

10. ____ 63 ____ | **11.** ____ 45 ____ | **12.** ____ 21 ____

13. ____ 34 ____ | **14.** ____ 57 ____ | **15.** ____ 82 ____

16. ____ 78 ____ | **17.** ____ 10 ____ | **18.** ____ 90 ____

 **Problem Solving** Solve. Use a strategy.

19. Derek has 23 balloons. Tina has 10 fewer balloons than Derek. How many balloons does Tina have?

____ balloons

20. Leah buys 36 plates and 30 cups. Then she buys 10 more plates. How many plates does Leah have?

____ plates

21. Ben made 29 hats. Sara made 10 fewer hats than Ben. Marco made 10 fewer hats than Sara. How many hats did Marco make?

____ hats

22. Julia has 12 red party horns. She has 10 more blue horns than red horns. How many party horns does Julia have in all?

____ party horns

Test Preparation

23. Write the number that is 10 more than 38. ____

Write the number that is 10 less than 84. ____

For additional Practice, go to page 261 in this Workbook.
Then go to Lesson 11-1B, pages 227–228 in this Workbook.

Objective: To subtract multiples of ten using the relationship between addition and subtraction

Mrs. Kim brings 50 apples to the school picnic. The children eat 30 apples.
How many apples are left?

Subtract: 50 − 30 = ?

50	20	50
−30	+30	−30
?	50	20

.....Think.....
| ? + 30 = 50 |
| 20 + 30 = 50 |

So, 50 − 30 = 20.

There are 20 apples left.

Use addition to find the difference.
Write the addition you use. Then write the difference.

1. 80 − 20 = ?

    60 + 20 = 80

    80 − 20 = 60

2. 90 − 50 = ?

    ___ + ___ = ___

    90 − 50 =

3.

50		50
−10	+☐	−10
?		

4.

60		60
− 40	+☐	− 40
?		

5. What addition sentence can you use to find 80 − 70? Why?

Use addition to find the difference.
Write the addition you use. Then write the difference.

6. 50 – 40 = ___   **7.** 90 – 60 = ___

___ + ___ = ___   ___ + ___ = ___

8. 60 – 20 = ___   **9.** 70 – 50 = ___

___ + ___ = ___   ___ + ___ = ___

10. 80 – 30 = ___   **11.** 40 – 40 = ___

___ + ___ = ___   ___ + ___ = ___

12. 70   ☐   **13.** 80   ☐   **14.** 90   ☐
      –30 + ☐   –10 + ☐   –70 + ☐

 **Problem Solving** Solve. Use a strategy.

15. Sam had 90 hats to sell. He sold some hats. Now he has 40 hats. How many hats did Sam sell?

____ hats

16. James bakes 80 muffins. He bakes 10 more muffins than June. How many muffins did June bake?

____ muffins

Test Preparation

17. What is the difference?

Write an addition sentence you can use to find the difference.

80 – 60 = ___

___ + ___ = ___

For additional Practice, go to page 262 in this Workbook.
Then go to Lesson 11-2, pages 505–506 in the Student Book.

Objective: To count back by tens or ones from a two-digit number

---

You can count back to subtract.

What is 3 less than 45?	What is 30 less than 45?

Start at 45.
Count back 3 ones.   (3 = 3 ones)

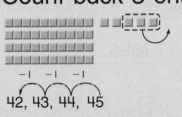

−1 −1 −1
42, 43, 44, 45

42 is 3 less than 45.

Start at 45.
Count back 3 tens.   (30 = 3 tens)

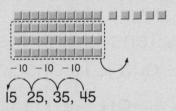

−10 −10 −10
15 25, 35, 45

15 is 30 less than 45.

Model each number. Count back by ones
to find the number that is less.

1. 2 less than 19

2. 3 less than 24

_____

3. 1 less than 38

_____

Model each number. Count back by tens
to find the number that is less.

4. 30 less than 68

_____

5. 20 less than 56

_____

6. 10 less than 30

_____

Talk It Over

7. Explain how to count back to find 20 less than 83.

Practice

Count back by ones to find the number that is less.
Use ▭▭▭▭▭ and ▪ to check.

8. 3 less than 76	**9.** 2 less than 52	**10.** 4 less than 27
_____	_____	_____
11. 3 less than 85	**12.** 1 less than 99	**13.** 4 less than 68
_____	_____	_____

Count back by tens to find the number that is less.
Use ▭▭▭▭▭ and ▪ to check.

14. 20 less than 84	**15.** 10 less than 29	**16.** 40 less than 97
_____	_____	_____
17. 30 less than 72	**18.** 40 less than 70	**19.** 20 less than 61
_____	_____	_____

Solve. Use a strategy.

20. Jean makes 3 fewer cards than Amad. Amad makes 28 cards. How many cards does Jean make?

Jean makes _____ cards.

21. Gavin uses two colors to make 36 hats. Some hats are blue. 20 hats are green. How many hats are blue?

_____ hats are blue.

What's the Error?

22. Ava says that 40 less than 84 is 80. What error did Ava make?

For additional Practice, go to page 263 in this Workbook.
Then go to Lesson 11-5, pages 511–512 in the Student Book.

Objective: To use bar models to solve subtraction problems within 100

There are 56 balloons.
Some balloons pop.
Now there are 44 balloons.
How many balloons pop?

The whole is 56.
One part is 44.
You need to find
the other part.
Subtract to solve.

Subtract: 56 − 44 = ?

12 balloons pop.

You can use a bar model
to help.

56

44   ?

$$\begin{array}{r} 56 \\ -44 \\ \hline 12 \end{array}$$

Use a bar model. Subtract to solve.

1. Emma makes 48 hats. Suki makes
23 fewer hats. How many hats
does Suki make?

Suki makes ____ hats.

2. Judy has 70¢. She spends 50¢
on a toy. How much money does
Judy have now?

Judy has ____ ¢ now.

3. How does the bar model help you know
which number to subtract from?

Name _____

Problem Solving Use a bar model. Subtract to solve.

4. Mr. Brown invites 62 friends to a party. 47 friends come to the party. How many friends do not come to the party?

_____ friends do not come.

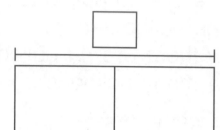

5. Gary has 75 toys for his party. He gives some away. Now he has 23 toys. How many toys does Gary give away?

Gary gives away _____ toys.

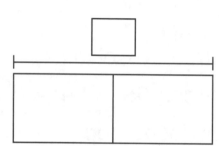

6. Angela has 97 party stickers. She has 21 more stickers than Frank. How many stickers does Frank have?

Frank has _____ stickers.

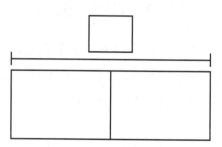

Explain Your Reasoning

7. Carl has 80¢. He buys a gift box. Does he have enough money to buy a card? Explain how you decided.

C For additional Practice, go to page 264 in this Workbook. Then go to Lesson 11-10, pages 523–524 in the Student Book.

Name _____

Objective: To compare one half, one third, and one fourth of the same whole

Tina and Eli have sheets of paper that are the same size. Tina folds her paper into fourths. She colors a quarter of her paper. Eli folds his paper into halves. He colors half of his paper.

One quarter is the same as one fourth.

Who colors the smaller part?

The paper with more equal parts has smaller parts.

$\frac{1}{4}$ is less than $\frac{1}{2}$.

Tina colors the smaller part.

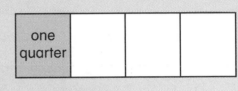

Color to show each fraction. Compare the fractions. Circle the fraction for the larger part.

1.

(one half)　one fourth

2. one fourth

one third

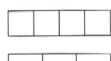

3.

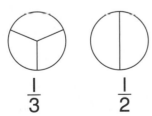

$\frac{1}{3}$ 　 $\frac{1}{2}$

4.

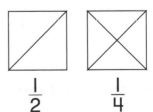

$\frac{1}{2}$ 　 $\frac{1}{4}$

5. Explain why one fourth of a pizza is smaller than one half of a pizza that is the same size.

Draw and color to show each fraction.
Compare the fractions.
Circle the fraction for the smaller part.

6. one fourth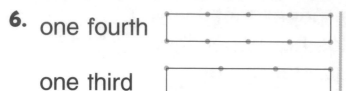

one third

7.

one quarter   one half

8. $\frac{1}{3}$

$\frac{1}{2}$

9. $\frac{1}{2}$

$\frac{1}{4}$

 Solve. Use a strategy.

10. Two crackers are the same size. Eva eats one half of her cracker. Ray eats one third of his cracker. Who eats more?

_____ eats more.

11. Two apples are the same size. Seth eats one fourth of his apple. Kate eats one half of her apple. Who eats less?

_____ eats less.

What's the Error?

12. Will cuts a ribbon into 2 equal pieces. Lisa cuts the same size ribbon into 3 equal pieces. Lisa says her pieces are longer because 3 is greater than 2. What is Lisa's error?

For additional Practice, go to page 265 in this Workbook. Then go to Lesson 12-5, pages 559–560 in the Student Book.

Additional CCSS Practice

Find Sums

Name _____

Look at the picture.
Put together and
to model a story.

$2 + 4 = 6$

There are 6 sheep in the pen.

Put together  and  to model each
addition story.

Write the addition sentence.

1.

3   +   3   =   6

2.

___   +   ___   =   ___

3.

___   +   ___   =   ___

4.

___   +   ___   =   ___

5.

___   +   ___   =   ___

6.

___   +   ___   =   ___

Use with Lesson 2-2A, pages 175–176 in this Workbook.
Then go to Lesson 2-3, pages 55–56 in the Student Book.

Equivalent Sums

Name _____

Add: 5 + 6

Break apart 6. →	Next add the doubles. →	Then add 1 more.
5 + 6	5 + 5 + 1	10 + 1 = 11
5 + 5 + 1	10 + 1	So, 5 + 6 = 11.

Break apart one addend. Add an easy fact first.

Find the sum. You can use ⬛ to help.

1. 4 +   5

4 + ___ + 1

___ + 1 = 9

So, 4 + 5 = ___.

2. 2 +   3

2 + ___ + 1

___ + 1 = 5

So, 2 + 3 = ___.

3. 3 + 4 = ?

___ + ___ + ___ = ___

4. 4 + 8 = ?

___ + ___ + ___ = ___

5. 5 + 7 = ?

___ + ___ + ___ = ___

6. 5 + 3 = ?

___ + ___ + ___ = ___

Use with Lesson 2-13A, pages 177–178 in this Workbook.
Then go to Lesson 2-14, pages 81–82 in the Student Book.

237

Solve Addition Word Problems

Name _____

Amy has 1 .

John has 2 .

Dee has 3 .

How many do they have in all?

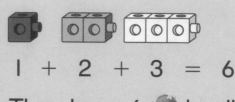

$1 + 2 + 3 = 6$

They have 6 in all.

Draw a picture or use .

Write an addition sentence to solve.

1. There are 3 on a plant.

There are 4 on a rock.

There are 2 on the ground.

How many are there in all?

___ + ___ + ___ = ___

There are ___ in all.

2. Fred finds 1 on a leaf.

Sue finds 5 on a stick.

Tim finds 1 under a rock.

How many do they find in all?

___ + ___ + ___ = ___

They find ___ in all.

3. Beth counts 2 in the barn. Ron counts 6 eating seeds. Greg counts 3 in a bush. How many do they count in all?

___ + ___ + ___ = ___

They count ___ in all.

4. Pat sees 5 small . He sees 4 big . He also sees 1 very big . How many does Pat see in all?

___ + ___ + ___ = ___

Pat sees ___ in all.

238

Solve for Unknowns

Name _____

You can draw ● to find a missing number.

$8 + \underline{} = 11$

11

11
●●● ●●● ●	

11
●●● ●●● ●	● ● ●

$\underline{8} + \underline{3} = \underline{11}$

Solve. Draw ● to help.

1. There are 4 🐱 sleeping.
Some 🐱 are eating.
There are 7 🐱 in all.
How many 🐱 are eating?

There are ____ 🐱 eating.

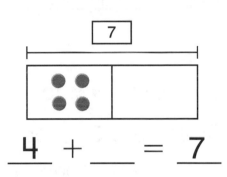

$\underline{4} + \underline{} = \underline{7}$

2. Steve puts some AB on the table.

He puts 5 AB on a chair.

Steve has 12 AB in all.

How many AB does Steve put on the table?

Steve puts ____ AB on the table.

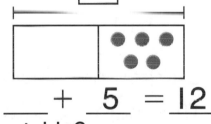

$\underline{} + \underline{5} = \underline{12}$

3. Alex sees 6 🐟 one day.

He sees 2 🐟 the next day.

How many 🐟 does Alex see?

Alex sees ____ 🐟.

4. There are 9 🐟 in a bowl.

Three of the 🐟 are small.

The rest are big.

How many big 🐟 are in the bowl?

There are ____ big 🐟.

☾ Use with Lesson 2-17A, pages 181–182 in this Workbook.
☾ Then go to Lesson 2-18, pages 89–90 in the Student Book.

239

Find Differences

Name _____

You can draw to find an unknown number.

$$6 - \underline{} = 2$$

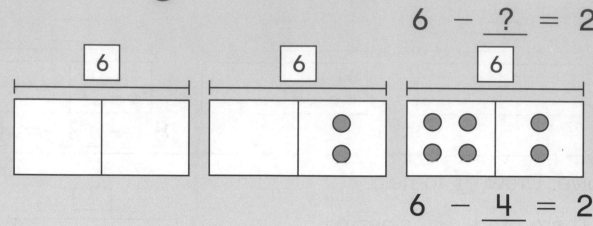

$$6 - \underline{4} = 2$$

Solve. Draw to help.

1. There are 5 🍒 on a table.

   A bird eats some 🍒.

   Now there are 3 🍒 on the table.

   How many 🍒 does the bird eat?

   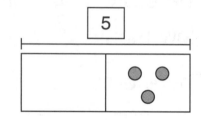

   $$\underline{5} - \underline{} = \underline{3}$$

   The bird eats ____ 🍒.

2. Children are playing with some ⚾.

   They put 4 ⚾ in a box.

   Now they have 2 ⚾.

   How many ⚾ did the children have to start?

   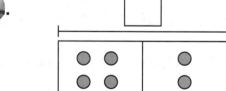

   The children had ____ ⚾ to start. $$\underline{} - \underline{4} = \underline{2}$$

3. Nancy has 4 🥨.

   She gives 1 🥨 to a friend.

   How many 🥨 does Nancy have left?

   Nancy has ____ 🥨 left.

C Use with Lesson 3-4A, pages 183–184 in this Workbook.
C Then go to Lesson 3-5, pages 109–110 in the Student Book.

Think Addition to Subtract

You can use a related addition fact
to help you find a difference.

Think:

$10 - 3 = ?$ $7 + 3 = 10$ So, $10 - 3 = 7$.

Use a related addition fact to find the difference.
Write the addition fact you use.
Then write the difference.

1. $8 - 6 = ?$

   ___ + ___ = ___

   $8 - 6 =$ ___

2. $12 - 5 = ?$

   ___ + ___ = ___

   $12 - 5 =$ ___

3.
   $\begin{array}{r} 9 \\ -\ 4 \\ \hline ? \end{array}$ $+ \Box$ $\begin{array}{r} 9 \\ -\ 4 \\ \hline \end{array}$

4.
   $\begin{array}{r} 6 \\ -\ 2 \\ \hline ? \end{array}$ $+ \Box$ $\begin{array}{r} 6 \\ -\ 2 \\ \hline \end{array}$

5. $10 - 2 =$ ___

   ___ + ___ = ___

6. $7 - 4 =$ ___

   ___ + ___ = ___

7.
   $\begin{array}{r} 11 \\ -\ 7 \\ \hline \end{array}$ $+ \Box$

8.
   $\begin{array}{r} 6 \\ -\ 3 \\ \hline \end{array}$ $+ \Box$

9.
   $\begin{array}{r} 9 \\ -\ 8 \\ \hline \end{array}$ $+ \Box$

Use with Lesson 3-11A, pages 185–186 in this Workbook.
Then go to Lesson 3-12, pages 125–126 in the Student Book.

241

Use a Bar Model

Name

Mike has 10 🍎.

Some of the 🍎 are green.

Seven 🍎 are red.

How many green 🍎 does Mike have?

Mike has 3 green 🍎.

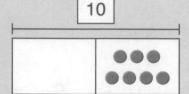
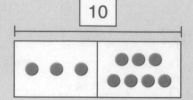

$10 - 7 = 3$

Solve. Draw ⬤ to help.
Write an addition or subtraction sentence.

1. There are 7 🦆. Five of the 🦆 are brown. The rest of the 🦆 are white. How many white 🦆 are there?

   _____ 🦆 are white.

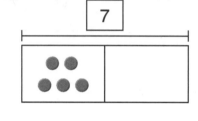

   _____ − _____ = _____

2. Jan has 6 red 🧢. She has 5 yellow 🧢. How many 🧢 does Jan have?

   Jan has _____ 🧢.

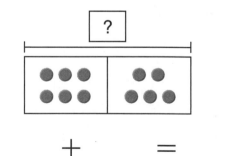

   _____ + _____ = _____

242

C Use with Lesson 3-12A, pages 187–188 in this Workbook.
C Then go to Lesson 3-13, pages 127–128 in the Student Book.

Data and Questions

Name _____

You can answer questions about data in graphs.

How many friends voted for 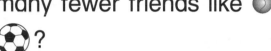?

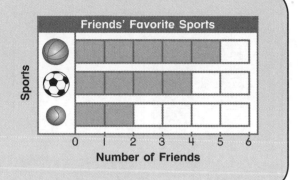

__2__ friends voted for .

Use the bar graph to answer the questions.

1. How many fewer friends like  than ?

   ____ ◯ ____ = ____

2. How many more friends like 🏀 than ⚾?

   ____ ◯ ____ = ____

3. How many fewer friends like ⚽ than 🏀?

   ____ ◯ ____ = ____

4. How many friends voted for a favorite sport?

   ____ ◯ ____ ◯ ____ = ____

5. One friend forgot to vote. Her favorite sport is ⚾. How many friends like  now?

   ____ ◯ ____ = ____

6. Use the data in the graph. Write a question. Answer the question.

   _____

Use with Lesson 4-7A, pages 189–190 in this Workbook.
Then go to Lesson 4-8, pages 173–174 in the Student Book.

243

Numbers to 120

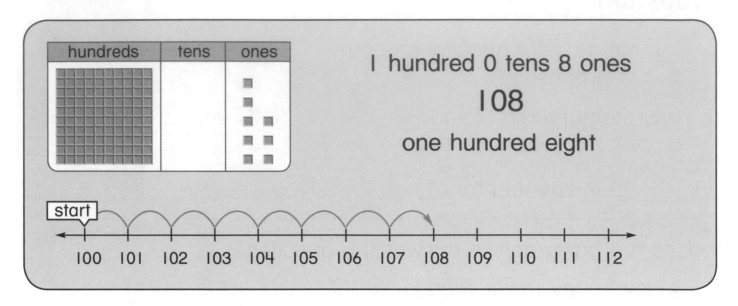

hundreds	tens	ones

1 hundred 0 tens 8 ones

108

one hundred eight

start
100 101 102 103 104 105 106 107 108 109 110 111 112

Use the model to write how many.

1.

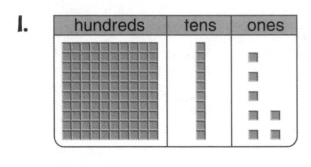

hundreds	tens	ones

_____ hundred _____ ten _____ ones

_____

2.

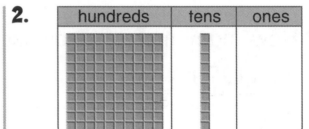

hundreds	tens	ones

_____ hundred _____ ten _____ ones

_____

Count by ones. Write the missing numbers.

3.

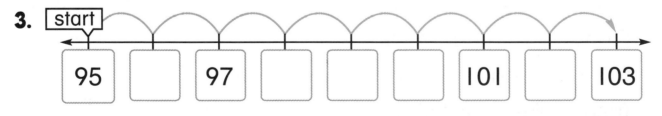

start
95 ___ 97 ___ ___ ___ 101 ___ 103

4.

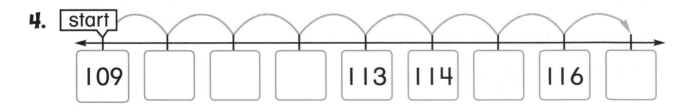

start
109 ___ ___ ___ 113 114 ___ 116 ___

Use with Lesson 5-7A, pages 191–192 in this Workbook.
Then go to Lesson 5-8, pages 211–212 in the Student Book.

Properties of Operations

When you change the order of the addends,
the sum is the same.

$8 + 5 = 13$　　　　　　　$5 + 8 = 13$

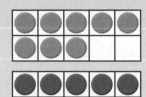　　　　　　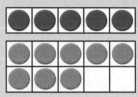

Find the sum. Change the order of the addends.
Find the sum again.

1. 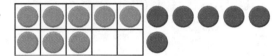　　　　

$8 + 6 = $ _____　　　　_____ + _____ = _____

---

2. $7 + 5 - $ _____

_____ + _____ = _____

3. $7 + 8 = $ _____

_____ + _____ = _____

---

4. $8 + 3 = $ _____

_____ + _____ = _____

5. $4 + 6 = $ _____

_____ + _____ = _____

6.
$$\begin{array}{r} 3 \\ + 9 \\ \hline \end{array}$$

7.
$$\begin{array}{r} 6 \\ + 7 \\ \hline \end{array}$$

8.
$$\begin{array}{r} 9 \\ + 7 \\ \hline \end{array}$$

ℂ Use with Lesson 6-2A, pages 193–194 in this Workbook.
ℂ Then go to Lesson 6-3, pages 261–262 in the Student Book.

Make 10 to Add

Name _____

You can make 10 to help find sums.

Add: $9 + 4$

Break apart 4. ⟶   Next add to   Then add 3 more.
                         make 10. ⟶

$9 + \quad 4$ $9 + 1 + 3$ $10 + 3 = 13$

$9 + 1 + 3$ $10 + 3$ So, $9 + 4 = 13$.

Break apart one addend to make 10.
Then find the sum. You can use counters to help.

1. $8 \quad + \quad 6 \quad = ?$

$8 \quad + \underline{\quad} + 4 = ?$

$\underline{\quad} + 4 = \underline{\quad}$

So, $8 + 6 = \underline{\quad}$.

2. $5 \quad + \quad 7 \quad = ?$

$5 \quad + \underline{\quad} + 2 = ?$

$\underline{\quad} + 2 = \underline{\quad}$

So, $5 + 7 = \underline{\quad}$.

3. $9 + 8 = ?$

$\underline{\quad} + \underline{\quad} + \underline{\quad} = \underline{\quad}$

4. $7 + 6 = ?$

$\underline{\quad} + \underline{\quad} + \underline{\quad} = \underline{\quad}$

5. $7 + 9 = ?$

$\underline{\quad} + \underline{\quad} + \underline{\quad} = \underline{\quad}$

6. $5 + 8 = ?$

$\underline{\quad} + \underline{\quad} + \underline{\quad} = \underline{\quad}$

Use with Lesson 6-3A, pages 195–196 in this Workbook.
Then go to Lesson 6-4, pages 263–264 in the Student Book.

Make 10 to Subtract   Name _____

You can make 10 to help subtract.

Subtract: $14 - 6$

Break apart 6. $\longrightarrow$ Next subtract 4 to make 10. $\longrightarrow$ Then subtract 2 more.

$14 - \quad 6$	$14 - 4 - 2$	$10 - 2 = 8$
$14 - 4 - 2$	$10 - 2$	So, $14 - 6 = 8$.

Subtract one part from the whole to make 10.
Then subtract the other part.

1. $18 - 9$

$18 - \underline{} - \underline{}$

$\underline{} - \underline{} = \underline{}$

So, $18 - 9 = \underline{}$.

2. $13 - 7$

$13 - \underline{} - \underline{}$

$\underline{} - \underline{} = \underline{}$

So, $13 - 7 = \underline{}$.

3. $11 - 6$

$11 - \underline{} - \underline{}$

$10 - \underline{} = \underline{}$

4. $14 - 9$

$14 - \underline{} - \underline{}$

$10 - \underline{} = \underline{}$

5. $16 - 8$

$16 - \underline{} - \underline{}$

$10 - \underline{} = \underline{}$

6. $15 - 6$

$15 - \underline{} - \underline{}$

$10 - \underline{} = \underline{}$

C Use with Lesson 6-7A, pages 197–198 in this Workbook.
C Then go to Lesson 6-8, pages 273–274 in the Student Book.

True and False Sentences

Name _____

A number sentence can be true or false.

= means is the same as

Is $7 + 6 = 13$ true or false?

Add $7 + 6$ to find out.
$7 + 6 = 13$
Does $13 = 13$? Yes.
$7 + 6$ is the same as 13.
So, $7 + 6 = 13$ is true.

Is $14 - 8 = 7$ true or false?

Subtract $14 - 8$ to find out.
$14 - 8 = 6$
Does $6 = 7$? No.
$14 - 8$ is not the same as 7.
So, $14 - 8 = 7$ is false.

Circle the number sentences that are true.
Cross out the number sentences that are false.

1. $9 = 16 - 7$	**2.** $6 + 6 = 14$	**3.** $8 + 3 = 3 + 8$
4. $15 - 8 = 14 - 7$	**5.** $20 = 8 + 12$	**6.** $5 + 3 + 5 = 13$
7. $12 - 7 = 4$	**8.** $13 - 5 = 8$	**9.** $6 = 16 - 9$
10. $7 + 4 = 4 + 6$	**11.** $19 = 19$	**12.** $8 + 6 = 14$
13. $20 - 10 = 10$	**14.** $17 - 10 = 8$	**15.** $16 = 9 + 9$
16. $2 + 4 + 6 = 12$	**17.** $13 = 4 + 9$	**18.** $7 + 5 = 5 + 7$

Use with Lesson 6-10A, pages 199–200 in this Workbook.
Then go to Lesson 6-11, pages 281–282 in the Student Book.

Add and Subtract to Compare

You can add or subtract to compare.

Lily has 6 red beads.
She has 5 more blue
beads than red beads.
How many blue beads
does Lily have?

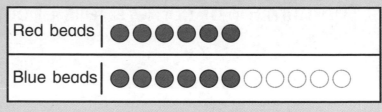

Red beads | ● ● ● ● ● ●

Blue beads | ● ● ● ● ● ● ○ ○ ○ ○ ○

$$6 + 5 = 11$$

Lily has 11 blue beads.

Draw ○ to compare. Then add or subtract to solve.

1. Matt reads 7 books. Tom
reads 15 books. How
many more books does
Tom read?

Matt |
Tom |

_____ − _____ = _____

Tom reads ____ more books.

2. Lisa buys 5 stamps. Ellen
buys 9 more stamps than
Lisa. How many stamps
does Ellen buy?

Lisa |
Ellen |

_____ + _____ = _____

Ellen buys ____ stamps.

3. Joe has 12 brown socks.
He has 4 fewer black
socks. How many black
socks does Joe have?

Brown |
Black |

_____ − _____ = _____

Joe has ____ black socks.

C Use with Lesson 6-11A, pages 201–202 in this Workbook.
Then go to Lesson 6-12, pages 283–284 in the Student Book.

249

Reason with Shapes

Name _____

The number of sides tells about the kind of figure.

The number of corners tells about the kind of figure.

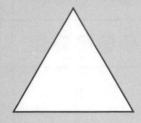

(3 sides)

(3 corners)

Circle the words that tell about the kind of figure.

Then draw the figure.

1. rectangle	4 corners yellow	**2.** triangle	small 3 sides
3. circle	0 sides big	**4.** pentagon	blue 5 corners
5. square	short 4 sides	**6.** triangle	3 corners tall

Use with Lesson 7-2A, pages 203–204 in this Workbook.
Then go to Lesson 7-3, pages 301–302 in the Student Book.

Ways to Make Plane Figures

Name _____

You can put together plane figures to make new plane figures.

Step 1	Step 2
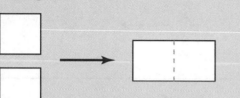	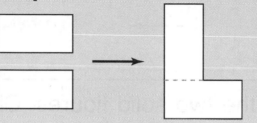

a. Draw a line to show how to use the plane figures to make a new figure.

b. Draw a line to show how to use two of the new figures to make another shape.

1. a.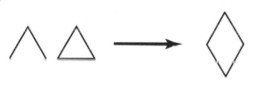

b.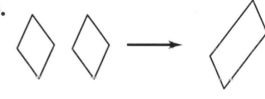

2. a.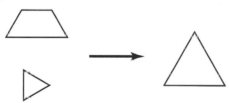

b.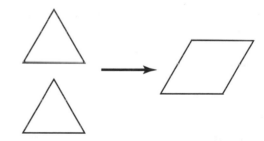

3. a.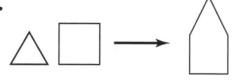

b.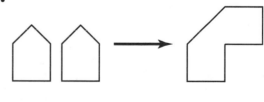

C Use with Lesson 7-3A, pages 205–206 in this Workbook.
C Then go to Lesson 7-4, pages 303–304 in the Student Book.

251

Ways to Make Solid Figures

You can put together solid figures to make new solid figures.

Step 1

Step 2

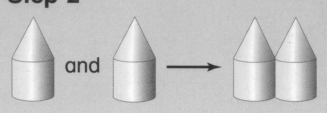

a. Use the two solid figures. Circle the new figure you can make.

b. Use two of the new figure from **a.** Circle the shape you can make.

l. a.

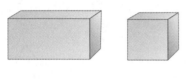

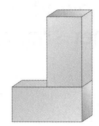  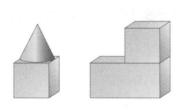

l. b.

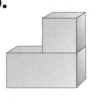

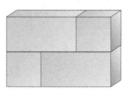 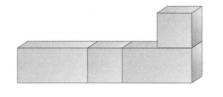

2. a.

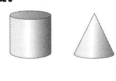

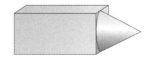 

2. b.

252

☞ Use with Lesson 7-5A, pages 207–208 in this Workbook.
☞ Then go to Lesson 7-6, pages 309–310 in the Student Book.

Length of a Path

Name _____

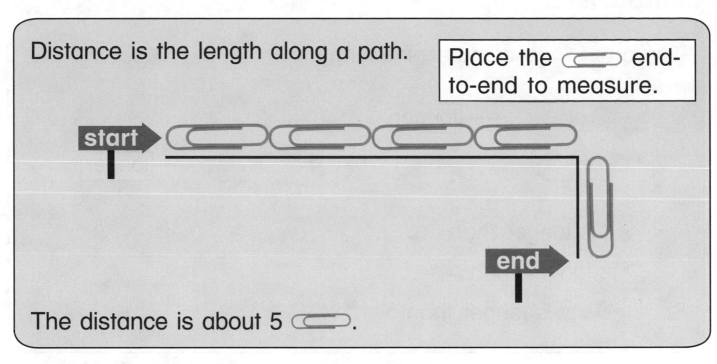

Distance is the length along a path.

Place the ⊂⊃ end-to-end to measure.

start ▶

end ▶

The distance is about 5 ⊂⊃.

Use ⊂⊃ to measure the distance along each path.

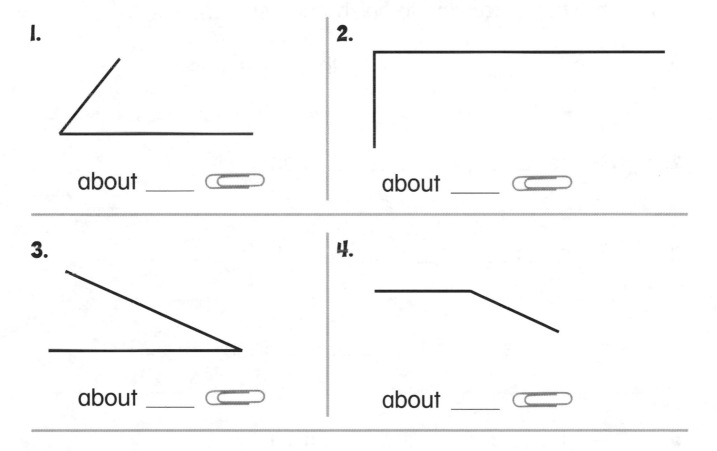

I.

about _____ ⊂⊃

2.

about _____ ⊂⊃

3.

about _____ ⊂⊃

4.

about _____ ⊂⊃

Use with Lesson 9-1A, pages 209–210 in this Workbook.
Then go to Lesson 9-2, pages 409–410 in the Student Book.

253

Use Indirect Comparison

Use a 🖇 to compare the lengths.

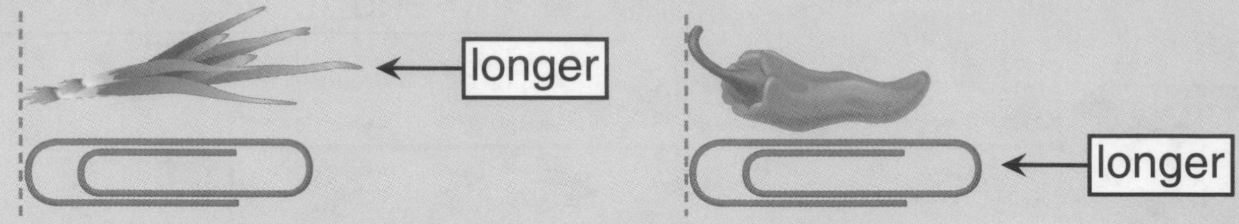

longer ←

longer ←

🌾 is longer than 🖇 .

🖇 is longer than 🌶 .

So, 🌾 is longer than 🌶 .

Compare the length of each picture to a small 🖇 . 
Write **shorter** or **longer** to finish each sentence.

I. 🥒 is _____ than 🫛 .

_____

2.  🥕 is _____ than 🌿 .

_____

3.  🌽 is _____ than 🥒 .

_____

4.  🫛 is _____ than 🥕 .

_____

5.  🥕 is _____ than 🥒 .

_____

C Use with Lesson 9-4A, pages 211–212 in this Workbook.
C Then go to Lesson 9-4B, pages 213–214 in this Workbook.

Use a Ruler

Name _____

Go to pages 213–214 in this Workbook. Use the ruler you made.

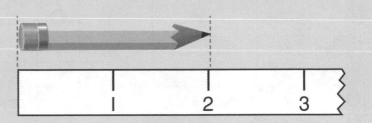

Use your ruler to measure the length of the .

Use your ruler to measure the length of each picture.

1.

about _____ unit

2.

about _____ units

3.

about _____ units

4.

about _____ units

5.

about _____ units

6.

about _____ units

C Use with Lesson 9-4B, pages 213–214 in this Workbook.
Then go to Lesson 9-5, pages 415–416 in the Student Book.

255

Add Using Drawings

62 + 13 = ?

Draw the addends.   Add the ones.   Then add the tens.

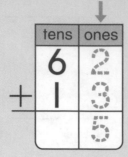

tens	ones

62 + 13 = 75

Add. Draw tens and ones to help.

1.
tens	ones
4	2
+ 3	3

tens	ones

2.
tens	ones
1	5
+ 2	4

tens	ones

3.
tens	ones
3	6
+ 5	0

tens	ones

4.
tens	ones
2	1
+ 4	7

tens	ones

5.
tens	ones
1	3
+ 1	4

tens	ones

6.
tens	ones
4	2
+ 5	2

tens	ones

C Use with Lesson 10-2A, pages 215–216 in this Workbook.
C Then go to Lesson 10-3, pages 469–470 in the Student Book.

Count On by Tens or Ones to Add

Name _____

What is 3 more than 62?

Start at 62. Count on 3 ones.

+1 +1 +1
62, 63, 64, 65

65 is 3 more than 62.

What is 30 more than 62?

Start at 62. Count on 3 tens.

+10 +10 +10
62, 72, 82, 92

92 is 30 more than 62.

Count on by ones to find the number that is more.

Use ▭▭▭▭▭▭▭▭▭ and ▪ to check.

1. 4 more than 23

2. 1 more than 54

3. 2 more than 61

___

___

___

4. 3 more than 76

5. 5 more than 12

6. 2 more than 30

___

___

___

Count on by tens to find the number that is more.

Use ▭▭▭▭▭▭▭▭▭ and ▪ to check.

7. 40 more than 49

8. 10 more than 32

9. 20 more than 23

___

___

___

10. 30 more than 64

11. 50 more than 36

12. 40 more than 17

___

___

___

13. 10 more than 71

14. 30 more than 45

15. 20 more than 50

___

___

___

C Use with Lesson 10-4A, pages 217–218 in this Workbook.
C Then go to Lesson 10-5, pages 473–474 in the Student Book.

Use Strategies to Add

You can use different strategies to add.

Count On to Add

Change the order of the addends if you need to.

$$\begin{array}{r} 30 \\ +16 \\ \hline ? \end{array} \qquad \begin{array}{r} 16 \\ +30 \\ \hline 46 \end{array}$$

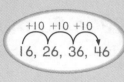

+10 +10 +10
16, 26, 36, 46

Break Apart to Add

Break apart one addend into tens and ones.

$$42 \rightarrow \begin{array}{c} 40 \\ 2 \end{array}$$

$$\begin{array}{r} 40 \\ + 5 \\ \hline ? \end{array} \qquad \begin{array}{r} 2 \\ + 5 \\ \hline ? \end{array} \qquad \begin{array}{r} 2 \\ 5 \\ + \end{array} \begin{array}{r} 40 \\ + 7 \\ \hline 47 \end{array}$$

Use a strategy to find the sum.

1. $\begin{array}{r} 46 \\ + 3 \\ \hline \end{array}$

2. $\begin{array}{r} 30 \\ +14 \\ \hline \end{array}$

3. $\begin{array}{r} 23 \\ + 5 \\ \hline \end{array}$

4. $\begin{array}{r} 60 \\ +27 \\ \hline \end{array}$

5. $\begin{array}{r} 20 \\ +32 \\ \hline \end{array}$

6. $\begin{array}{r} 71 \\ + 4 \\ \hline \end{array}$

7. $\begin{array}{r} 50 \\ +18 \\ \hline \end{array}$

8. $\begin{array}{r} 91 \\ + 2 \\ \hline \end{array}$

9. $\begin{array}{r} 32 \\ + 7 \\ \hline \end{array}$

10. $\begin{array}{r} 24 \\ + 2 \\ \hline \end{array}$

11. $\begin{array}{r} 60 \\ +21 \\ \hline \end{array}$

12. $\begin{array}{r} 40 \\ +34 \\ \hline \end{array}$

Use with Lesson 10-5A, pages 219–220 in this Workbook.
Then go to Lesson 10-5B, pages 221–222 in this Workbook.

Add 2-Digit Numbers

You can use different strategies to add. $26 + 32 = ?$

One Way to Add	Another Way to Add
Break apart one addend into tens and ones.	Break apart both addends into tens and ones.

One Way to Add:

$$\begin{array}{r} 26 \\ + \boxed{32} \\ \hline ? \end{array} \rightarrow \begin{array}{r} 26 \\ \boxed{30} \\ 2 \\ \hline ? \end{array} \rightarrow \begin{array}{r} 56 \\ + 2 \\ \hline 58 \end{array}$$

Another Way to Add:

$$\begin{array}{r} 26 \\ + 32 \end{array} \rightarrow \begin{array}{r} \boxed{20} + \boxed{6} \\ + \boxed{30} + \boxed{2} \\ \hline ? \quad\quad 50 + 8 = 58 \end{array}$$

Use a strategy to find the sum.

1. $\begin{array}{r} 63 \\ +25 \\ \hline \end{array}$ **2.** $\begin{array}{r} 21 \\ +34 \\ \hline \end{array}$ **3.** $\begin{array}{r} 18 \\ +51 \\ \hline \end{array}$

4. $\begin{array}{r} 32 \\ +14 \\ \hline \end{array}$ **5.** $\begin{array}{r} 54 \\ +43 \\ \hline \end{array}$ **6.** $\begin{array}{r} 45 \\ +23 \\ \hline \end{array}$

7. $\begin{array}{r} 25 \\ +22 \\ \hline \end{array}$ **8.** $\begin{array}{r} 12 \\ +63 \\ \hline \end{array}$ **9.** $\begin{array}{r} 73 \\ +23 \\ \hline \end{array}$

10. $\begin{array}{r} 18 \\ +21 \\ \hline \end{array}$ **11.** $\begin{array}{r} 32 \\ +37 \\ \hline \end{array}$ **12.** $\begin{array}{r} 44 \\ +22 \\ \hline \end{array}$

Use with Lesson 10-5B, pages 221–222 in this Workbook.
Then go to Lesson 10-6, pages 475–476 in the Student Book.

Bar Models and Addition Problems

Name _____

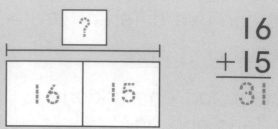

Mr. Ray's class has 16 girls.
Mr. Ray's class has 15 boys.
How many children are
in Mr. Ray's class?

There are 31 children in Mr. Ray's class.

Complete the bar model. Add to solve.

1. Kim planted 33 pumpkin seeds.
Then she planted 19 more pumpkin
seeds. How many seeds did Kim
plant in all?

_____ seeds

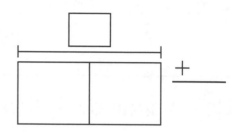

2. Mr. Tan cooked some hotdogs for a
picnic. He cooked 28 beef hotdogs.
He cooked 45 turkey hotdogs. How
many hotdogs did Mr. Tan cook?

_____ hotdogs

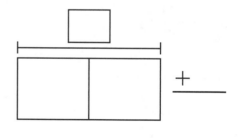

3. Pedro has 47 car models. He has
14 fewer car models than his brother.
How many car models does his
brother have?

_____ car models

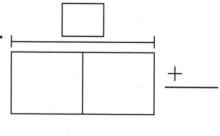

4. Beth read 64 pages of a book. Mary
read 26 more pages than Beth. How
many pages did Mary read?

_____ pages

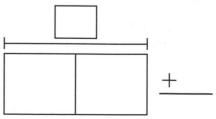

Use with Lesson 10-10A, pages 223–224 in this Workbook.
Then go to Lesson 10-11, pages 487–488 in the Student Book.

Mental Math: Ten More or Ten Less

Name _____

What number is 10 less than 53?
What number is 10 more than 53?

Count back 10.   Count on 10.

43   53   63

43 is 10 less than 53.   63 is 10 more than 53.

Use mental math.
Write the number that is 10 less.
Then write the number that is 10 more.

1. ___ 65 ___	**2.** ___ 49 ___	**3.** ___ 24 ___
4. ___ 37 ___	**5.** ___ 81 ___	**6.** ___ 50 ___
7. ___ 23 ___	**8.** ___ 76 ___	**9.** ___ 42 ___
10. ___ 54 ___	**11.** ___ 30 ___	**12.** ___ 17 ___
13. ___ 88 ___	**14.** ___ 62 ___	**15.** ___ 75 ___

Use with Lesson 11-1A, pages 225–226 in this Workbook.
Then go to Lesson 11-1B, pages 227–228 in this Workbook.

Subtract Multiples of 10

Name _____

You can use addition to help you subtract.
Subtract 70 − 30 = ?

$$\begin{array}{r} 70 \\ -30 \\ \hline ? \end{array} \qquad \begin{array}{r} ? \\ +30 \\ \hline 70 \end{array} \qquad \begin{array}{r} 40 \\ +30 \\ \hline 70 \end{array} \qquad \begin{array}{r} 70 \\ -30 \\ \hline 40 \end{array}$$

So, 70 − 30 = 40.

Use addition to find the difference.
Write the addition you use. Then write the difference.

1. 60 − 10 = ____
   ____ + ____ = ____

2. 80 − 40 = ____
   ____ + ____ = ____

3. 40 − 30 = ____
   ____ + ____ = ____

4. 50 − 20 = ____
   ____ + ____ = ____

5. 70 − 40 = ____
   ____ + ____ = ____

6. 90 − 30 = ____
   ____ + ____ = ____

7. $\begin{array}{r} 80 \\ -60 \\ \hline \end{array}$ ☐ $+$ ☐

8. $\begin{array}{r} 90 \\ -40 \\ \hline \end{array}$ ☐ $+$ ☐

9. $\begin{array}{r} 60 \\ -60 \\ \hline \end{array}$ ☐ $+$ ☐

10. $\begin{array}{r} 50 \\ -40 \\ \hline \end{array}$ ☐ $+$ ☐

11. $\begin{array}{r} 70 \\ -10 \\ \hline \end{array}$ ☐ $+$ ☐

12. $\begin{array}{r} 40 \\ -20 \\ \hline \end{array}$ ☐ $+$ ☐

C Use with Lesson 11-1B, pages 227–228 in this Workbook.
Then go to Lesson 11-2, pages 505–506 in the Student Book.

Count Back by Tens or Ones to Subtract

Name _____

What is 3 less than 59?

Start at 59.
Count back 3 ones.

−1 −1 −1

56 57 58 59

56 is 3 less than 59.

What is 30 less than 59?

Start at 59.
Count back 3 tens.

−10 −10 −10

29 39 49 59

29 is 30 less than 59.

Count back by ones to find the number that is less.
Use 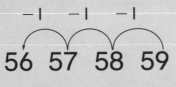 and ▪ to check.

1. 2 less than 65   _____

2. 4 less than 28   _____

3. 3 less than 37   _____

4. 1 less than 52   _____

5. 3 less than 46   _____

6. 5 less than 77   _____

Count back by tens to find the number that is less.
Use 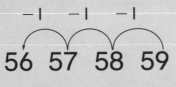 and ▪ to check.

7. 40 less than 98   _____

8. 20 less than 55   _____

9. 10 less than 29   _____

10. 30 less than 64   _____

11. 40 less than 93   _____

12. 50 less than 92   _____

13. 10 less than 77   _____

14. 20 less than 80   _____

15. 30 less than 48   _____

C Use with Lesson 11-4A, pages 229–230 in this Workbook.
C Then go to Lesson 11-5, pages 511–512 in the Student Book.

Bar Models and Subtraction Problems

Name _____

There are 49 balloons.
Some balloons pop.
Now there are 36 balloons.
How many balloons pop?

13 balloons pop.

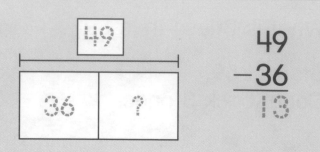

$$\begin{array}{r} 49 \\ -36 \\ \hline 13 \end{array}$$

Use a bar model. Subtract to solve.

1. There are 64 cars in the school parking lot. Some cars drive away. Now there are 31 cars in the parking lot. How many cars drove away?

_____ cars drove away.

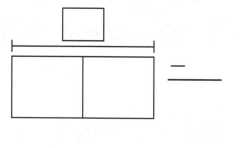

2. Gabe has 38 crayons. Trish has 24 fewer crayons. How many crayons does Trish have?

Trish has _____ crayons.

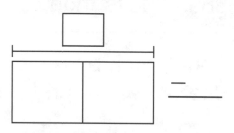

3. Ms. Teller bakes 72 cookies. She gives some to friends. Now she has 42 cookies. How many cookies did Ms. Teller give to friends?

Ms. Teller gave _____ cookies to friends.

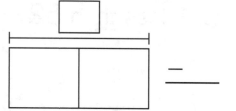

4. Chris has 87¢. He spends 62¢ on a sticker. How much money does Chris have now?

Chris has _____ ¢ now.

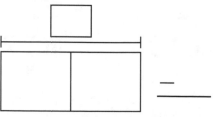

264

Compare Fractions

Name _____

The rectangles are the same size.
Which shaded part is smaller?

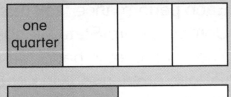
One quarter is the same as one fourth.

$\frac{1}{4}$ is less than $\frac{1}{2}$.

One quarter is smaller than one half.

| one quarter | | | |

| one half | |

Draw and color to show each fraction.
Circle the fraction for the larger part.

1.
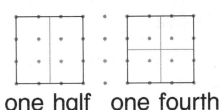
one half   one fourth

2.
one fourth   one half

Draw and color to show each fraction.
Circle the fraction for the smaller part.

3. $\frac{1}{4}$
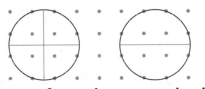

$\frac{1}{3}$

4. $\frac{1}{4}$

$\frac{1}{2}$

5.
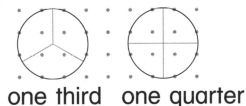
one third   one quarter

6.
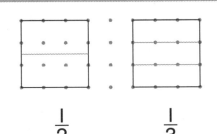

$\frac{1}{2}$ $\frac{1}{3}$

C Use with Lesson 12-4A, pages 233–234 in this Workbook.
Then go to Lesson 12-5, pages 559–560 in the Student Book.

Dear Student,

Pages 268–282 of this workbook have Performance Tasks that let you show your understanding of the Common Core math taught in *Progress in Mathematics*.

Each performance task has five parts. The content of each part meets the Common Core State Standards (CCSS) for *Progress in Mathematics* lessons. The goal of each performance task is for you to apply critical thinking skills and various problem-solving strategies to the math content learned in the chapters. The Performance Tasks are useful tools for evaluating your understanding of Grade 1 math and the Common Core State Standards. You will find the Performance Tasks on the following pages.

Performance Task 1: Chapters 1–4   pages 268–272

Performance Task 2: Chapters 5–8   pages 273–277

Performance Task 3: Chapters 9–12   pages 278–282

Your teacher will use a rubric in the Teacher's Edition of this workbook to record your understanding of Common Core State Standards.

Performance Task Contents

C Performance Task I
The Great Marble Match

I There is a big game at the park.

Six children are playing with .

Two more children join them.

Then 4 more children join them.

How many children are playing with ?

Here are some strategies you can use.

- Draw a picture.
- Count on.
- Write addition facts.
- Make ten.

Show your work.

_____ children are playing with .

C Performance Task I
Lucy's Lost Marbles

Name _____

2 Lucy has 9 .

She loses some of them in the grass.

Now she has 5 .

How many does Lucy lose in the grass?

- Use the bar model.
- Write a subtraction sentence.
- Add to check your answer.
- Write your related addition sentence.

Show your work.

Lucy loses _____ in the grass.

C Performance Task 1
Peter's Puzzle

Name _____

3 Peter has red and blue .

He has 10 in all.

At least 3 are blue.

How many blue could Peter have?

How many red could he have?

- Fill in the addition chart.
- Look for a pattern. Describe the pattern.
- Write an addition fact for each answer.
- Write a related subtraction fact for each addition fact.

Show your work.

Addend	Addend	Sum

The pattern is _____.

Peter could have _____ or _____ blue .

He could have _____ or _____ red .

C Performance Task 1
What a Game!

Name _____

4 Three children have marbles on the ground.

- Tally to show how many marbles of each kind.
- Make a pictograph from your tally chart.

How many more than are on the ground?

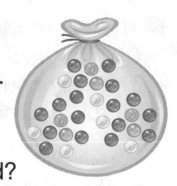

Show your work.

Kinds of Marbles		
Marble	**Tally**	**Number**
●		
◐		
○		

Kinds of Marbles	
●	
◐	
○	
Key : Each ○ stands for 1 marble.	

There are _____ more than on the ground.

C Performance Task I
The Final Tally

Name _____

5 The Great Marble Match is over.
Children are walking home.
The tally chart shows how many
marbles some children have.

- Make a bar graph from the tally chart.

- Write some questions you can answer
  by reading the graph.

- Write a question comparing how many
  marbles two children have.

- Answer each question.

- Write a subtraction sentence for your
  comparing question.

Show your work.

Marble Collections	
Child	**Tally**
Lisa	ЖᎢ ‖
Bill	‖‖
Tim	ЖᎢ	
Sue	ЖᎢ ‖‖

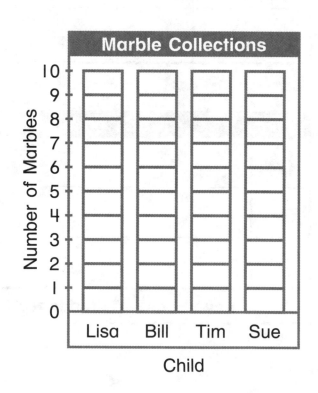

Marble Collections

Number of Marbles: 10 9 8 7 6 5 4 3 2 1 0

Lisa Bill Tim Sue

Child

C Performance Task 2
Super Stamp Collections

I Many children collect .

Some children collect old .

Some children collect new .

You can collect  from all over the world!

Derek has this many .

Rita has 59 .

- Write how many  Derek has.
- Write the value of each digit in Derek's number of .
- Write Rita's number of  in expanded form.
- Compare the numbers. Write $<$, $=$, or $>$.

Derek gives 10 of his  to Rita.

Who has more  now?

Show your work.

_____ has more now.

C Performance Task 2
More Stamps for Sam

Name _____

2 Sam has 5 .

His mom gives him 6 more .

Then his dad gives him 4 more .

How many does Sam have now?

Here are some strategies you can use.

- Draw a picture.
- Change the order of the addends.
- Make 10.
- Use a doubles fact.

Show your work.

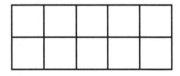

Sam has _____ now.

C Performance Task 2
Stella Uses Stamps!

Name _____

 Stella writes cards to send to friends.

She has 17 .

Stella puts 8  on the cards.

She mails the cards.

How many  does Stella have now?

- Make 10 to subtract.
- Write a subtraction fact.
- Add to check your answer.
- Write the rest of the related facts in the fact family.

Show your work.

Stella has _____ now.

4 Nick collects from many countries.

His are many colors.

His are many sizes.

The are shaped like plane figures.

Nick wants to make a bar graph.

The graph will show the kinds of plane figures in his stamp collection.

- Make a bar graph to show Nick's stamp collection.
- Write a question that can be answered by looking at the graph.
- Answer your question.

Show your work.

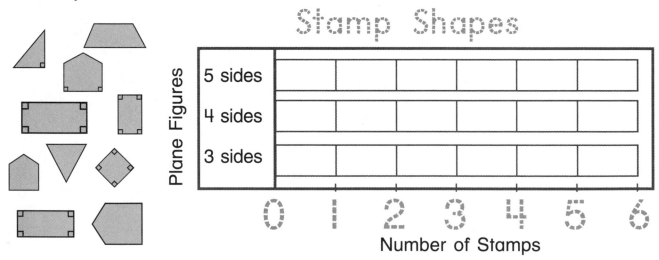

Stamp Shapes

Plane Figures	0	1	2	3	4	5	6
5 sides							
4 sides							
3 sides							

Number of Stamps

5 Meg is going to the Stamp Fair.

She will see old stamps.

She will see rare stamps.

Meg will see stamps that are worth a lot of money!

The Stamp Fair starts at 1:00.

The clocks show when she sees the stamps.

Meg leaves the fair at half past 2.

- Write the time Meg sees each kind of stamp.
- Draw arrows to show the path Meg takes.
- Draw the hands on the clock to show when Meg leaves the fair.

Show your work.

Old Stamps

_____

Rare Stamps

_____

New Stamps

_____

Meg leaves the fair at _____.

Performance Task 3
Green Hill Vegetable Stand

1 Fran's family lives on Green Hill Farm.

They have animals.

They grow 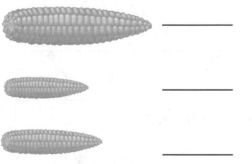 and other vegetables.

They sell fresh vegetables at a stand.

Help Fran put  and  in boxes.
Use  to measure.

- Compare the lengths of the vegetables in each group.
- Order the vegetables from shortest to longest.
- Write **1st**, **2nd**, and **3rd**.
- Then measure the boxes.
- Draw lines to show which two boxes Fran will use.

Show your work.

 _____

 _____

 _____

 _____

 _____

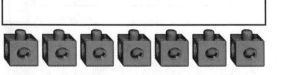

Performance Task 3

Name ______________________

Peppers, Peppers, Everywhere!

2 The farm has a field of .

Fran picks  every day.

On Tuesday, Fran picks 43 .
Then she picks 26 more .

On Wednesday, Fran picks 30 .
Then she picks 37 more .

On which day does Fran pick more ?

Here are some strategies you can use.

- Use  and .
- Use an addition frame.
- Break apart the addends.
- Count on.

Show your work.

	tens	ones
+		

tens	ones

	tens	ones
+		

Fran picks more  on ______________.

C Performance Task 3
How Much Money?

Name _____

3 Mr. Kane buys two .

Fran weighs the  to find how much they cost.

The large ⬭ costs 38¢.

The small ⬭ costs 23¢.

How much do the ⬭ cost in all?

Here are some strategies you can use.

- Use a bar model.
- Use an addition frame.
- Use ▬▬▬▬ and ▪ .
- Use 🪙 and 🪙 .
- Break apart the addends.

Show your work.

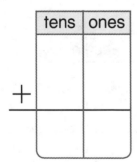

tens	ones
+	

The ⬭ cost _____ in all.

4 A blue box has 80 .

Fran sells 50 from the blue box.

A green box has 60 .

Fran sells 40 from the green box.

Ms. Landers wants to buy 30 .

Which box of should Fran sell to her?

Here are some strategies you can use.

- Use ▬▬▬▬▬ or 🪙.
- Count back.
- Use addition.
- Use bar models.

Show your work.

Fran should sell the _____ box of to Ms. Landers.

5 Fran makes a  bread.

She also makes a 🎃 bread.

The breads are the same size.

Fran cuts the  bread into 4 equal parts.

She cuts the 🎃 bread into 2 equal parts.

Wendy buys 1 part of the  bread.

Theo buys 1 part of the 🎃 bread.

Who buys more bread?
How many parts of each bread are left?

• Show how Fran cuts the  bread.

• Show how Fran cuts the 🎃 bread.

• Color the parts that Fran sells.

Show your work.

 **Bread**	🎃 **Bread**

_____ buys more bread.

_____ parts of the  bread are left.

_____ part of the 🎃 bread is left.